How Green Is My Church?

By
Christopher Dunphy

Published by

The Green Apostle Ltd
PO Box 630
Rochdale OL16 9HJ

©the green apostle ltd

Index

1	Introduction	4
2	Global Warming and Climate Change	7
3	Getting Started	25
4	Church Audit	37
5	Energy Efficiency	41
6	Heating	45
6.1	Fuel	57
6.2	Boilers	62
6.3	Other Forms of Heat	64
7	Renewable Energies	67
7.1	Solar	68
7.2	Heat Pumps	75
7.3	Geothermal	78
7.4	Wind Technology	83
7.5	Biomass	86
8	Environmentally Friendly Shopping	93
9	Recycling	102
10	Greening up the Churchyard	116
11	Your Parish and the Community	119
12	The Wider Community	122
13	Conclusions	124
14	United Reformed Church Resolution 19	126
15	Further sources of Information	135

Introduction

We have all heard about Global warming usually conjuring up images of fierce storms, severe and extreme weather, rising sea levels and flooding a doomsday scenario straight out of Revelations. Unfortunately this image is one of our own making, as it is caused by our burning vast amounts fossil fuels for energy releasing carbon dioxide into the atmosphere; so much our vastly reduced forests and woodlands can not absorb it.

We have caused the problem and it is our collective responsibility to put it right. The bible has much to say on human responsibility for the planet from when we are first given stewardship of the earth in Genesis.

Then God said: "Let us make man in our image and let them rule over the fish of the sea and the birds of the air, over the livestock, over all the earth and over all the creatures that move along the ground." (Genesis 1:26)

In Ezekiel we are warned against abusing our position as stewards.

Woe to the shepherds of Israel who only take care of themselves! Should not the shepherds take care of the flock? You eat the curds, clothe yourselves with the wool and slaughter the choice animals, but you did not take care of the flock! You have not strengthened the weak or healed the sick or bound up the injured. You have not brought back the strays or searched for the lost. You have ruled them harshly and brutally. (Ezekiel 34:2-4.)

In the story of Noah, God explicitly asks Noah to save every kind of living creature and once the floodwaters recede makes a covenant blessing and protecting every living species, as stewards of his creation we are expected to do the same

Then God said to Noah and to his sons with him: "I now establish my covenant with you and your descendants after you and with every living creature that was with you - the birds, the livestock and all the wild animals, all those that came out of the ark with you - every living Creature on the earth."
(Genesis 9:8-9)

Climate change is the biggest threat facing humanity today. God gave us this planet to look after and in the last few hundred years we've done a poor job of it. We have been wiping out countless species, pumping greenhouse gasses into the atmosphere, as well as poisoning the land with toxic chemicals and radioactivity.

Following God's teachings and protecting the environment and the remaining wildlife is reason enough to cut carbon emissions. But reducing the carbon footprint does not just help the environment but will enable us to pass on the planet to the next generation in the same condition as we received it, surely the goal of not just a steward, but of any responsible person.

The more we speak out and show our commitment towards helping the environment the more governments and international committees will listen and implement changes in legislation to help the environment and encourage research and funding into renewable energy sources, recycling and the like.

When I started on this project my objective was to try and produce a definitive guide to show how a church could identify and relate with the environmental issues of today and how they could implement them into their own community. As I actually got into writing the book I realised that some things needed a little more explanation than others. I really have tried to keep it simple, but along the way the subject became more complicated, I felt there was a need to try to fully explain all the mysteries and buzz words you hear everyday but may not have fully understood. So please bear with me there are some technical parts that unfortunately we cannot get away from.

There would have been little point in producing a book that just sent you running to the library or 'Google' to investigate further, so I hope I have hit the right balance between being technical and being informative.

This book is designed to get you started and help you identify where you and your community can make a real difference.

Global Warming and Climate Change

I think we need to start by explaining what global warming is. We hear about it almost everyday of our lives, probably so much that we tend to switch off and could be forgiven for indulging in the knowledge that someone else will understand or take care of it. That time has now passed and we all need to take action. So what exactly is Climate Change?

Temperatures provide the clearest evidence that the climate is changing and globally the average temperature has risen by more than 0.7°C over the last 100 years.

The natural greenhouse gas effect keeps our planet much warmer than it would otherwise be, without it Earth would be extremely cold. Greenhouse gases such as carbon dioxide (CO_2), methane and water vapour behave like a blanket around our planet. These gases allow the sun's rays to reach the surface of the Earth, but impede the heat they create from escaping back into space.

Any increase in the levels of greenhouse gas in the atmosphere mean that more heat is trapped and global temperatures increase - an effect known as 'global warming'.

There is indisputable evidence that this observed global warming is predominantly caused by increases in greenhouse gas concentrations. Concentrations of CO_2, created largely by the burning of fossil fuels, are now much higher and are increasing at a much faster rate than at any time in the last 500,000 years.

As CO_2 is a greenhouse gas, the increased concentrations have contributed to the recent warming and probably most of the warming over the last 50 years

The rise in global surface temperature has averaged more than 0.15°C per decade since the mid-1970s. Warming has been unprecedented in at least the last 50 years or so and the 17 warmest years on record have all occurred in the last 20 years. This does not necessarily mean that next year will be warmer than last year, but the long-term trend is for rising temperatures, to me this is hard evidence that seems indisputable.

A simple mathematical calculation of the temperature change over the latest decade alone shows a continued warming of 0.1°C per decade. The recent slight slowing of the warming is due to a shift towards more frequent La Nina conditions in the Pacific since 1998. These bring cool water up from the depths of the Pacific Ocean, cooling global temperatures.

1998 saw an exceptional El Niño event, which contributed strongly to that record-breaking year. Research shows that an exceptional El Niño can warm global temperatures by about 0.2°C in a single year. 2005 was also an unusually warm year, the second highest in the global record, but it was not associated with the El Niño conditions that boosted the warmth of 1998.

Another way of looking at the warming trend is that 1999 was a similar year to 2007 as far the cooling effects of La Niña are concerned.

The 1999 global temperature was 0.26°C above the 1961-90 average, whereas 2007 was 0.37°C above this average, 0.11°C warmer than 1999.

Our climate is complex and influenced by many things, particularly changes in orbit, volcanic eruptions and changes in the energy emitted from the sun. It is well known that the world has experienced warm or cold periods in the past without any interference from humans. The ice ages are good examples of global changes to the climate and warm periods have seen grapes grown across much of Britain.

Over the several hundred thousand years covered by the ice core record, the temperature changes were primarily driven by changes in Earth's orbit around the sun. Over this period, changes in temperature did drive changes in CO_2. Since the Industrial Revolution (over the last 100 years), CO_2 concentrations have increased by 30% due to human induced emissions from fossil fuels.

The bottom line is that temperature and CO_2 concentrations are linked. In recent ice ages, natural changes in the climate, such as those due to orbit changes, led to cooling of the climate system. This caused a fall in CO_2 concentrations, which weakened the greenhouse effect and amplified the cooling. Now the link between temperature and CO_2 is working in the opposite direction. Human induced increases in CO_2 are driving the greenhouse effect and are amplifying the recent warming.

There are many factors that may contribute to climate change. Only when all of these factors are included do we get a satisfactory explanation of the magnitude and patterns of climate change over the last century.

Over the last 1,000 years most of the variability can probably be explained by cooling due to major volcanic eruptions and changes in solar heating.

In the 20th century the situation becomes more complicated. There is some evidence that increases in solar heating may have led to some warming early in the 20th century, but direct satellite measurements show no appreciable change in solar heating over the last three decades. Three major volcanic eruptions in 1963, 1982 and 1991 led to short periods of cooling. Throughout the century, CO_2 increased steadily and has been shown to be responsible for most of the warming in the second half of the century.

As well as producing CO_2, burning fossil fuels also produces small particles called aerosols, which cool the climate by reflecting sunlight back into space. These have increased steadily in concentration over the 20th century, which has probably offset some of the warming we have seen.

Changes in solar activity do affect global temperatures, but research has shown that over the last 50 years, increased greenhouse gas concentrations have a much greater effect than changes in the sun's energy.

The global average temperature will increase by 2 to 3°C this century – according to one of the Intergovernmental Panel on Climate Change's (IPCC). This rise in temperature means that the Earth will experience a greater climate change than it has for at least 10,000 years and it would be difficult for many people and ecosystems to adapt to this rapid change.

These temperature increases are likely to result in an increased frequency and severity of weather events such as heatwaves, storms and flooding.

Rising levels of greenhouse gases in the atmosphere could set in motion large-scale changes in Earth's natural systems. Some of these could be irreversible — the melting of large ice sheets will result in major consequences for low-lying areas throughout the world.

Climate change is any long-term significant change in the "average weather" that a particular region experiences. Average weather may include average temperature, precipitation and wind patterns. It involves changes in the variability or average state of the atmosphere over durations ranging from decades to millions of years. These changes can be caused by dynamic process on Earth, external forces including variations in sunlight intensity and more recently by human activities.

In recent usage, especially in the context of environmental policy, the term "climate change" often refers to changes in modern climate.

Climate changes reflect variations within the Earth's atmosphere, processes in other parts of the Earth such as oceans and ice caps and the effects of human activity. The external factors that can shape climate are often called climate forcings and include such processes as variations in solar radiation, the Earth's orbit and greenhouse gas concentrations.

Weather is the day-to-day state of the atmosphere and is a chaotic non-linear dynamical system Climate the average state of weather; is fairly stable and predictable.

Climate includes the average temperature, amount of precipitation, days of sunlight and other variables that might be measured at any given site. However, there are also changes within the Earth's environment that can affect the climate.

Glaciers are recognized as being among the most sensitive indicators of climate change, advancing substantially during climate cooling (e.g. the Little Ice Age[1]) and retreating during climate warming on moderate time scales. Glaciers grow and collapse, both contributing to natural variability and greatly amplifying externally forced changes. For the last century however, glaciers have been unable to regenerate enough ice during the winters to make up for the ice lost during the summer months

The most significant climate processes of the last several million years are the glacial and interglacial cycles of the present ice age. Though shaped by orbital variations, the internal responses involving continental ice sheets and 130m sea-level change certainly played a key role in deciding what climate response would be observed in most regions. Other changes, including Heinrich events[2], Dansgaard–Oeschger events[3] and the Younger Dryas[4], show the potential for glacial variations to influence climate even in the absence of specific orbital changes.

More generally, most forms of internal variability in the climate system can be recognized as a form of hysteresis, meaning that the current state of climate reflects not only the inputs, but also the history of how it got there. For example, a decade of dry conditions may cause lakes to shrink, plains to dry up and deserts to expand. In turn, these conditions may lead to less rainfall in the following years. In short, climate change can be a self-perpetuating process because different aspects of the environment respond at different rates and in different ways to the fluctuations that inevitably occur.

Current studies indicate that radiative forcing by greenhouse gases is the primary cause of global warming. Greenhouse gases are also important in understanding Earth's climate history. According to these studies the greenhouse effect, which is the warming produced as greenhouse gases trap heat, plays a key role in regulating Earth's temperature.

Over the last 600 million years, CO_2 levels have varied from perhaps 5000 parts per million (ppm) to less than 200ppm, due primarily to the effect of geological processes and biological innovations. It has been argued, that variations in greenhouse gas concentrations over tens of millions of years have not been well correlated to climate change, with plate tectonics perhaps playing a more dominant role.

There are several examples of rapid changes in the concentrations of greenhouse gases in the Earth's atmosphere that do appear to correlate to strong warming, including the Paleocene–Eocene Thermal Maximum[5], the Permian-Triassic Extinction Event[6] and the end of the Varangian Snowball Earth Event[7].

During the modern era, the naturally rising CO_2 levels are implicated as the primary cause of global warming since 1950.

According to the Intergovernmental Panel on Climate Change (IPCC), 2007, the atmospheric concentration of CO_2 in 2005 was 379ppm compared to the pre-industrial levels of 280 ppm. Thermodynamics and Le Chatelier's principle[8] explain the characteristics of the dynamic equilibrium of a gas in solution such as the vast amount of CO_2 held in solution in the world's oceans moving into and returning from the atmosphere. These principles can be observed as bubbles which rise in a pot of water heated on a stove, or in a glass of cold beer allowed to sit at room temperature; gases dissolved in liquids are released under certain circumstances.

On the longest time scales, plate tectonics will reposition continents, shape oceans, build and tear down mountains and generally serve to define the stage upon which climate exists. More recently, plate motions have been implicated in the intensification of the present ice age when, approximately 3 million years ago, the North and South American plates collided to form the Isthmus of Panama and shut off direct mixing between the Atlantic and Pacific Oceans.

Variations in solar activity during the last several centuries based on observations of sunspots and beryllium isotopes.

The sun is essentially the ultimate source of all heat in the climate system. The energy output of the sun, which is converted to heat at the Earth's surface, is an integral part of shaping the Earth's climate.

On the longest time scales, the sun itself is getting brighter with higher energy output; as it continues its main sequence, this slow change or evolution affects the Earth's atmosphere. It is thought that, early in Earth's history, the sun was too cold to support liquid water at the Earth's surface, leading to what is known as the Faint Young Sun paradox[9].

On more modern time scales, there are also a variety of forms of solar variation, including the 11-year solar cycle and longer-term modulations. However, the 11-year sunspot cycle does not show itself clearly in the climatological data. Solar intensity variations are considered to have been influential in triggering the Little Ice Age[1] and for some of the warming observed from 1900 to 1950. The cyclical nature of the sun's energy output is not yet fully understood; it differs from the very slow change that is happening within the sun as it ages and evolves.

In their effect on climate, orbital variations are in some sense an extension of solar variability, because slight variations in the Earth's orbit lead to changes in the distribution and abundance of sunlight reaching the Earth's surface. Such orbital variations, known as Milankovitch cycles, are a highly predictable consequence of basic physics due to the mutual interactions of the Earth, its moon and the other planets. These variations are considered the driving factors underlying the glacial and interglacial cycles of the present ice age. Subtler variations are also present, such as the repeated advance and retreat of the Sahara desert in response to orbital precession.

With volcanoes a single eruption of the kind that occurs several times per century can affect climate, causing cooling for a period of a few years. For example, the eruption in 1991 of Mount Pinatubo on the island of Luzon in the Philippines affected the climate substantially. Huge eruptions, known as large igneous provinces, occur only a few times every hundred million years, but can reshape climate for millions of years and cause mass extinctions. Initially, scientists thought that the dust emitted into the atmosphere from large volcanic eruptions was responsible for the cooling by partially blocking the transmission of solar radiation to the Earth's surface. However, measurements indicate that most of the dust thrown in the atmosphere returns to the Earth's surface within six months.

Volcanoes are also part of the extended carbon cycle. Over very long (geological) time periods, they release carbon dioxide from the Earth's interior, counteracting the uptake by sedimentary rocks and other geological carbon dioxide sinks. However, this contribution is insignificant compared to the current anthropogenic emissions. The US Geological Survey estimates that human activitiy generates more than 130 times the amount of CO_2 emitted by volcanoes.

Anthropogenic factors are human activities that change the environment and influence climate. In some cases the chain of causality is direct and obvious (e.g. the effects of irrigation on temperature and humidity), while in others it is less clear. Various hypotheses for human induced climate change have been debated for many years.

The biggest factor of present concern is the increase in CO_2 levels due to emissions from fossil fuel combustion, followed by aerosols (particulate matter in the atmosphere), which exert a cooling effectand cement manufacture. Other factors, including land use, ozone depletion, animal agriculture and deforestation also affect climate.

Beginning with the industrial revolution in the 1850s and accelerating ever since, the human consumption of fossil fuels has elevated CO_2 levels from a concentration of ~280ppm to more than 380ppm today. These increases are projected to reach more than 560ppm before the end of the 21st century. It is known that carbon dioxide levels are substantially higher now than at any time in the last 750,000 years. Along with rising methane levels, these changes are anticipated to cause an increase of 1.4°C – 5.6°C between 1990 and 2100

Anthropogenic aerosols, particularly sulphate aerosols from fossil fuel combustion, exert a cooling influence. This together with natural variability, is believed to account for the relative "plateau" in the graph of 20th-century temperatures in the middle of the century.

Cement manufacturing is the third largest cause of man-made carbon dioxide emissions. Carbon dioxide is produced when calcium carbonate is heated to produce the cement ingredient calcium oxide. While fossil fuel combustion and deforestation each produce significantly more carbon dioxide, cement-making is responsible for approximately 2.5% of total worldwide emissions from industrial sources (energy plus manufacturing sectors).

Prior to the widespread use of fossil fuel the biggest effect that humanity had on local climate is likely to have been from land use. Irrigation, deforestation and agriculture fundamentally change the environment. For example, they change the amount of water going into and out of a given location. They also may change the local albedo[10] by influencing the ground cover and altering the amount of sunlight that is absorbed. There is evidence to suggest that the climate of Greece and other Mediterranean countries was permanently changed by widespread deforestation between 700 BC and 1 AD the wood was being used for shipbuilding, construction and fuel, with the result that the modern climate in the region is significantly hotter and drier, also the species of trees that were used for shipbuilding in the ancient world can no longer be found in the area.

In modern times a 2007 Jet Propulsion Laboratory study found that the average temperature of California has risen about 2° over the past 50 years, with a much higher increase in urban areas. The change was attributed mostly to extensive human development of the landscape

If certain forcings (for example, solar variation) acts to change the climate, then there may be mechanisms that act to amplify or reduce the effects. These are called positive and negative feedbacks. As far as is known, the climate system is generally stable with respect to these feedbacks.

However, a number of important positive feedbacks do exist. The glacial and interglacial cycles of the present ice-age provide an important example.

It is believed that orbital variations provide the timing for the growth and retreat of ice sheets. However, the ice sheets themselves reflect sunlight back into space and hence promote cooling and their own growth, known as the ice-albedo[10] feedback. Further, falling sea levels and expanding ice decrease plant growth and indirectly lead to declining CO_2 and methane. This leads to further cooling. Conversely, rising temperatures caused, for example, by anthropogenic emissions of greenhouse gases could lead to decreased snow and ice cover, revealing darker ground underneathand consequently result in more absorption of sunlight.

Water vapor, methane and CO_2 can also act as significant positive feedbacks, their levels rising in response to a warming trend, thereby accelerating that trend. Water vapor acts strictly as a feedback (excepting small amounts in the stratosphere), unlike the other major greenhouse gases, which can also act as forcings.

More complex feedbacks include heat movement from the equatorial regions to the northern latitudes and involve the possibility of altered water currents within the oceans or air currents with in the atmosphere. A significant concern is that melting glacial ice from Greenland may interfere and change the thermohaline[11] circulation of water in the North Atlantic, affecting the Gulf Stream which brings warmer water to replace sinking colder water; which would change the distribution of heat to Europe and the east coast of the United States.

Other potential feedbacks are not as well understood and may either inhibit or promote warming. For example, it is unclear if rising temperatures promote or inhibit vegetative growth, which could in turn draw down either more or less carbon dioxide. Similarly, increasing temperatures may lead to either more or less cloud cover. Since on balance cloud cover has a strong cooling effect, any change to the abundance of clouds also affects climate.

Scientists use "Indicator time series" that represent the many aspects of climate and ecosystem status. The time history provides a historical context. Current status of the climate is also monitored with climate indices.

Evidence for climatic change is taken from a variety of sources that can be used to reconstruct past climates. Most of the evidence is indirect—climatic changes are inferred from changes in indicators that reflect climate, such as vegetation, dendrochronology[12] and palynology[13]. Palynology is used to infer the geographical distribution of plant species, which vary under different climate conditions. Different groups of plants have pollen with distinctive shapes and surface texturesand since the outer surface of pollen is composed of a very resilient material, they resist decay. Changes in the type of pollen found in different sedimentation levels in lakes, bogs or river deltas indicate changes in plant communities; which are dependent on climate conditions.

Remains of beetles are common in freshwater and land sediments. Different species of beetles tend to be found under different climatic conditions.

Knowledge of the present climatic range of the different species and the age of the sediments in which remains are found, allows past climatic conditions to be inferred.

Advancing glaciers leave behind moraines and other features that often have datable material in them, recording the time when a glacier advanced and deposited a feature. Similarly, by tephrochronological techniques[14], the lack of glacier cover can be identified by the presence of datable soil or volcanic tephra horizons. Glaciers are considered one of the most sensitive climate indicators by the IPCCand their recent observed variations provide a global signal of climate change

The life cycles of many wild plants and animals are closely linked to the passing of the seasons; climatic changes can lead to interdependent pairs of species (e.g. a wild flower and its pollinating insect) losing synchronization, if for example, one has a cycle dependent on day length and the other on temperature or precipitation. In principle at least, this could lead to extinctions or changes in the distribution and abundance of species. One phenomenon is the movement of species northwards in Europe. A recent study by Butterfly Conservation in the U.K. has shown that relatively common species with a southerly distribution have moved north, whilst scarce upland species have become rarer and lost territory towards the south. This picture has been mirrored across several invertebrate groups. Drier summers could lead to more periods of drought, potentially affecting many species of animal and plant.

For example, in the UK during the drought year of 2006 significant numbers of trees died or showed dieback on light sandy soils. In Australia since the early 90s, tens of thousands of flying foxes have died as a direct result of extreme heat. Wetter, milder winters may affect temperate mammals or insects by preventing them hibernating or entering torpor during periods when food is scarce.

One predicted change is the ascendancy of 'weedy' or opportunistic species at the expense of scarcer species with narrower or more specialized ecological requirements. One example could be the expanses of bluebell seen in many types of woodland in the UK. These have an early growing and flowering season before competing weeds can develop and the tree canopy closes. Milder winters can allow weeds to 'over' winter as adult plants or germinate sooner, whilst trees leaf earlier, reducing the length of the window for bluebells to complete their life cycle. Organisations such as Wildlife Trust[A], World Wide Fund for Nature[B], Birdlife International[C] are actively monitoring and research the effects of climate change on biodiversity and advance policies in areas such as landscape scale conservation to promote adaptation to climate change.

1 The Little Ice Age: A cooling period that occurring after a period known as the Medieval Warm Period dated approximately from the 16th century to the mid 19th century. It is generally agreed that there were three, beginning about 1650, about 1770, and 1850, each separated by slight warming intervals.

2 Heinrich Events: Named after marine geologist Hartmut Heinrich who first described such events. Icebergs containing rock mass broke away from glaciers and moved into the North Atlantic as they melted the rock-mass fell to the sea floor as 'ice-rafted debris'

3 Dansgaard-Oeschger Events: Rapid climate changes occurring approx every 2000 years or so throughout the last glacial period. Twenty-three such events have been identified

4 Younger Dryas: Also refered to as the Big Freeze. A rapid climate change period detected from layers in North European bog peat.

5 Paleocene-Eocene Thermal Maximum: This event saw global temperatures rise by around 6 C over 20,000 years, sea levels rose as the whole of the oceans warmed. Atmospheric CO_2 concentrations rose as a result.

6 Permian–Triassic Extinction Event: Also known informally as the Great Dying. It was Earth's most severe extinction event that happened 251.4million years ago, up to 96 percent of all marine species became extinct.

7 Varangian Snowball Earth Hypothesis: The original hypothesis suggests that Earth had been entirely covered by ice 790 to 630 million years ago. It was developed to explain some enigmatic features of the Cryogenian geological record

8 Le Chatelier's Principle: Named after Henry Louis Le Chatelier. It can be used to predict the effect of a change on a chemical balance.

9 Faint Young Sun Paradox: In Earth's early history it is a possible contradiction between observations of water and the assumption that the heat generated from the sun would only be 70% as intense during that time compared to modern time.

10 Albedo: Reflectivity. The extent of which a surface diffusely reflects light from the sun.

11 Thermohaline circulation: Thermo- refers to temperature and -haline refers to salt content, which together determine the density of sea water.

12 Dendrochronology: Tree ring dating

13 Palynology: Study of pollen, spores and palynomorphs

14 Tephrochronology: Uses layers of tephra-volcanic ash from a single eruption, to create a chronological framework.

A The Wildlife Trust
The Kiln
Waterside
Mather Road
Newark
NG24 1WT
Tel: 01636 677711
Email: enquiry@wildlifetrusts.org

B World Wildlife Fund
Panda House
Weyside Park
Godalming
Surrey GU7 1XR
Tel: 01483 426444
Fax: 01483 426409

C Birdlife International
The Lodge
Sandy
Bedfordshire
SG19 2DL
Email: info@rspb.org.UK
Web: http://www.rspb.org.uk

3 Getting started

For the best part of thirty years now, I have been visiting churches throughout the country as my prime business has been the design of heating systems for churches. I am sure most people would agree that I have one of the better jobs in the country.

I have always has a great love of religious buildings and I have had a very rewarding career comforted by the knowledge I have been instrumental in helping to protect our heritage for future generations.

I guess that interest started at St John's R.C. church in Rochdale in the fifties. St John's was not my local church, but I was at St John's school next door and we attended a weekly Mass and other services officiated by the rather daunting Monsignor Kelly. He would come around school every Monday morning and question us on Sunday's sermon to see whether we had attended Mass like good Catholics! We didn't dare miss.

St John's is a large church built in the Byzantine style, similar in design to the Blue Mosque in Istanbul, but on a much smaller scale. In those days there were no microphones or sound systems and St John's has a seven and a half second echo. This meant that in reality I could not hear a word after the opening seven seconds, which left me with no option but to peruse every detail of the church's architecture.

It could well be that Monsignor Kelly is responsible for my current career, although be it by default.

The main role of my business to date has been advising churches on the heating and fabric protection of the building, now the role of helping protect the churches fabric has been extended to helping protect the environment. This is the new challenge to which we all must rise.

It sounds daunting when put it like that doesn't it? Well it need not be. It is all a matter of re-education, what seems a mammoth task today will hopefully become second nature to the next generation.

We all have become aware of the changing vocabulary, carbon footprints, global warming, greenhouse gasses and climate change. When I was at school there were just sunny days and rainy days. Now we get floods of biblical proportion, if you forgive the pun and temperatures that seem to produce new 'highs' almost every year.

So what is a carbon footprint?

The carbon footprint is a measure of the exclusive global amount of carbon dioxide and other greenhouse gases emitted by a human activity or accumulated over the full life cycle of a product or service.

The life cycle concept of the carbon footprint means that it is all encompassing and includes all possible causes that give rise to carbon emissions. In other words, all direct (on-site, internal) and indirect emissions (off-site, external, embodied, upstreamand downstream) need to be taken into account.

Normally, a carbon footprint is expressed as a CO_2 equivalent (usually in kilograms or tonnes), which accounts for the same global warming effects of different greenhouse gases. Carbon footprints can be calculated using a Life Cycle Assessment (LCA) method, or can be restricted to the immediately attributable emissions from energy use of fossil fuels.

An alternative definition of the carbon footprint is the total amount of carbon dioxide attributable to the actions of an individual (mainly through their energy use) over a period of one year. This definition underlies the personal carbon calculators. The term owes its origins to the idea that a footprint is what has been left behind as a result of the individual's activities. Carbon footprints can either consider only direct emissions (typically from energy used in the home and in transport, including travel by cars, airplanes, rail and other public transport), or can also include indirect emissions (including CO_2 emissions as a result of goods and services consumed). Bottom-up calculations sum the attributable amount of CO_2 emissions from individual actions; top-down calculations take total emissions from a country (or other high-level entity) and divide these emissions among the residents (or other participants in that entity). In summery then a Carbon Footprint is made up of the sum of two parts, the primary footprint and the secondary footprint.

The primary footprint is a measure of our direct emissions of CO_2 from the burning of fossil fuels including domestic energy consumption and transportation.

The secondary footprint is a measure of the indirect CO_2 emissions from the whole lifecycle of products we use - those associated with their manufacture and eventual breakdown.

When we look at green issues in the church then the biggest opportunity for reducing our primary carbon footprint is usually down to the energy consumption on lighting and heating. The lighting is remedied quite easily, which I will explain later, the heating however is far more complex and again I will cover this in detail later in the book.

In both cases this will reduce our primary carbon footprint and this has an immediate impact on the environment.

Carbon dioxide emissions to air (and the emissions of other greenhouse gasses) are almost exclusively associated with the conversion of energy carriers like natural gas, crude oil, etc. The carbon content released during the energy conversion process reaches the atmosphere and is deemed to be responsible for the global warming process (i.e. climate change).

The Kyoto Protocol[1] defines legally binding targets and timetables for cutting the greenhouse-gas emissions of industrialized countries that ratified the Kyoto Protocol[1]. Accordingly, from an economic or market perspective, one has to distinguish between a mandatory market and a voluntary market. It is typical for both markets is the trade with emission certificates

The mandatory market has to reach the goals defined in the Kyoto Protocol[1] with least economical costs the following flexible mechanisms were introduced for the mandatory market, these include Emissions Trading, Clean Development and Joint Implementation

In contrast to the strict rules set out for the mandatory market, the voluntary market provides companies with different options to acquire emissions reductions. A solution, comparable with those developed for the mandatory market, has been developed for the voluntary market, the Verified Emission Reductions (VER). This measure has the great advantage that the projects/activities are managed according to the quality standards set out for Clean Development Market (CDM)[2]/Joint Implementation (JI)[3] projects but the certificates provided are not registered by the governments of the host countries or the Executive Board of the United Nations Organisation (UNO). As such, high quality VERs can be acquired at lower costs for the same project quality. However, at present VERs can not be used in the mandatory market.

There are project developers, wholesalers, brokers and retailers, as well as carbon funds in the voluntary market. Some businesses and non-profiteers in the voluntary market encompass more than just one of the activities listed above. A report by Ecosystem Marketplace[4] shows that carbon offset prices increase as it moves along the supply chain from project developer to retailer.

While some mandatory emission reduction schemes exclude forest projects, these projects flourish in the voluntary markets. A major criticism concerns the imprecise nature of greenhouse gasses. The sequestration, quantification, and methodologies for forestry projects. However, others note the community co-benefits that forestry projects foster. Project types in the voluntary market range from avoided deforestation, reforestation, industrial gas sequestration, increased energy efficiency, fuel switchingand methane capture from coal plants and livestockand even renewable energy.

Renewable Energy Certificates (RECs) sold on the voluntary market are quite controversial due to additional concerns. Industrial Gas projects receive criticism because such projects only apply to large industrial plants that already have high fixed costs. Siphoning off industrial gas for sequestration is considered picking the low hanging fruit; which is why credits generated from industrial gas projects are the cheapest in the voluntary market.

The size and activity of the voluntary carbon market is difficult to measure. The most comprehensive report on the voluntary carbon markets to date was released by Ecosystem Marketplace and New Carbon Finance in July of 2007.

The good news is that when we get to grips with lowering our carbon footprint on the church heating and lighting, we are also reducing our energy costs, so that any monies spent in this area are usually self-funding in a relatively short period of time.

It might be useful to know that there are now many bodies that grant aid projects that specifically target reducing the carbon footprint.

So how do we get started?

Many churches and religious organisations from all denominations have various initiatives, projects and conferences on environmental issues, some of which you may already have heard of and are well worth checking out. It is an excellent start as they will give you an idea of what other Christian organisations and churches are doing and have a whole host of information and resources as well as advice. There is a resources section at the end of this book devoted to websites and addresses of useful contacts and organisations that can help you along the way.

The Church of England has its own environmental policy and has pledged to reduce its carbon emissions by 40% by the year 2050 through it's shrinking the footprint initiative. This involves following the shrinking the footprint path, which has 6 steps:

1) Each church assessing their carbon footprint.
2) Saving/reducing energy.
3) Switch to greener energy.
4) Switching to renewable energy source.
5) Offset carbon emissions.
6) Starting at the beginning to reduce footprint further.

The United Reformed Church have teamed up with the Methodist Church of Great Britain, each having their own environmental policy and others, including Christian Aid[A] and A Rocha[B] in a network of environmentally minded churches and Christian organisations whose aim is to spread the environmental message throughout the Christian community. They have come together under the name 'Creation Challenge'

Both the Baptist and Roman Catholic Churches also have their own environmental policies.

A Rocha[B] is an international Christian nature conservation organisation that carries out conservation projects and research all over the world and supports churches in the UK in taking action to help the environment.

The Operation Noah[C] mission is to get the churches in the UK and the Government to lead a move towards a liveable and sustainable lifestyle for the entire population. Originally, Operation Noah was a collaboration between Christian Ecology link and the Environmental Issues Network of Churches together in Britain and Ireland, it is now a separate charity in its own right.

If you are aiming to reduce your church carbon emissions it is important to know how much you are using at the present so that you have a benchmark to see how much you have reduced your carbon footprint, this is particularly vital if you have a particular target in mind.

An environmental audit will not only give you this benchmark but give you pointers and ideas on the areas you need to work on and is an excellent place to start.

Reducing your primary carbon footprint has an immediate impact and your audit will reveal many areas were savings can and should be made. The secondary footprint is every bit as important and relates as much to life style and re-education in the smaller, but no less important matters, such as travelling, packaging and dealing with waste.

When people are talking about environmental issues, they assume that everyone will know what they are talking about and understand all the 'buzz' words. Well if you do not, then I will try to explain all the things you need to know.

For instance you may have heard of carbon offsetting and wondered what exactly it was without wanting to ask. Well, carbon offsetting can be used to compensate for the emissions used by making an equivalent carbon dioxide saving somewhere else.

To carbon offset you first need to calculate how much carbon your footprint is creating, to do this you need a carbon calculator. This is probably better if it is done on line; you will find details of how to do this in the resources section at the end of this book.

Once you have done this you then buy offset credits from emission reduction projects. These projects will reduce or have already reduced carbon emissions elsewhere in the world.

There are two types of carbon credits, certified and voluntary credits. Certified Emission Reduction (CER) products are Kyoto Protocol compliant and are fully traceable. They will have been verified by the United Nations.

European Union Allowances (EUA) can be 'retired'; this is achieved by buying up all the available credits. Offsetting in this way reduces the amount of carbon dioxide allowance available for the largest polluting companies to buy. The EUA's would otherwise be traded on to Companies to help them to meet their emissions targets. By buying these offsets you are encouraging organisations to continue to make savings of CO_2 and pushing the market to make it increasingly expensive for polluting companies to buy more credits.

Voluntary carbon credits go to projects such as international tree planting programmes. In simple terms, trees breathe in carbon dioxide and breathe out oxygen. Trees also have the benefit of providing sustainable eco-environments. They provide a habitat for wildlife and encourage biodiversity.

You should always ensure with voluntary offsetting that the carbon offsetting is suitably verified or a well-known and accredited body, again there are suitable references in the resources section at the end of the book.

Now we have the basics it is time to start looking around our church and looking at where we can implement effective changes. We also need to look at the way we manage the day to day running of the church, the impact on the community and indeed our own lifestyle. As responsible stewards we need to set examples to the rest of the church community. This is our church audit and our starting point.

1 Kyoto Protocol: An international framework convention on Climate Change with the objective of reducing greenhouse gases in an effort to prevent anthropogenic climate change.

2 Clean Development Mechanism (CDM): An arrangement under the Kyoto Protocol allowing industrialised countries with a greenhouse gas reduction commitment (called Annex 1 countries) to invest in projects that reduce emissions in developing countries as an alternative to more expensive emission reductions in their own countries.

3 Joint implementation (JI): One of three flexibility mechanisms set forth in the Kyoto Protocol

4 Ecosystem Marketplace: An organisation that hopes to become theworld's leading source of information on markets and payment schemes for ecosystem services.

35

Ecosystem Marketplace
Tel: 001(415) 315-9011
Fax: 001 (415) 354-8450
E-mail: info@ecosystemmarketplace.com

A Christian Aid
35 Lower Marsh
London
SE1 7RL
Tel: +44 (0)20 7620 4444
Email:info@christian-aid.org

B A Rocha
3 Hooper St
Cambridge
CB1 2NZ
Tel: 01387 710286

C Operation Noah
The Grayston Centre
28 Charles Square
London
N1 6HT
Tel:020 7324 4761 or 020 7324 4769
Mobile: 07968 131 639

4 Church Audits

The first step toward becoming carbon neutral is to conduct an Environmental Audit. This will tell you exactly what you are good at and which areas you need to work on. It also gives a baseline that will allow you to measure your progress. It is also a good place to get realistic ideas on how to make changes.

Audits can be carried out yourself or a professional auditor can come and do it for you and will then explain the results. Professional environmental auditors can usually be found through your local council.

'How Green in my Church' is an audit book that is available and it is an excellent tool in your environmental challenge. Starting outside the church and looking at all aspects of efficiency, this book takes you through an audit step by step. As well as providing ideas it is a great stimulus to get your thought process into gear for the challenges ahead.

To get a general idea and starting point on how your church is doing when addressing environmental issues try tackling the following questions:

- How often have environmental issues been brought up within the last year during a service, bible study, house groups, children's groups etc?

- How often are environmental issues addressed in worship? For example hymns with environmental theme, either praising Gods creation or out calling to protect the environment? Outdoor services/Prayer walks?

If the answers to the previous questions are:

- Never - then you should perhaps consider including environmental issues into church services and activities.

- Once or twice a year at special services - you have made a start but definitely need to do more.

- Infrequently - more than six times a year, then you are doing okay but could probably do more.

- Frequently – once a month or more, that is excellent!

These questions show how aware you and your congregation are of environmental issues. The main thing is spreading the word because we can only save the planet if we all act together; does your church do this enough?

Other questions you could ask are:

- Does your church use green energy from a renewable source i.e. wind or solar power?

- Does your church monitor energy consumption monthly? If so, what is it and do you understand what your consumption should be or indeed how you can improve it?

- Do you monitor monthly fuel consumption on church vehicles? What is it? Do you have a management programme for vehicles?

These types of questions are some of the most important as they make you think about how much fuel you use.

It is easy to forget that it is not only the church building that uses fuel, it also includes the fuel used to make and transport everything the church uses and buys. Once you engage in the process of identifying areas of waste you will be surprised just how many savings can be made – even in a very small church.

Try answering these questions:

- Does your church use locally sourced produce?

- Do you serve organic bread and wine for communion or fair-trade tea and coffee after services?

- Are the heating and water systems regularly serviced?

- Are timers set correctly

- Do you have draft excluders for doors? Curtains for windows etc?

- Do you have appropriate insulation where possible?

- Have you installed low energy light bulbs throughout the church complex?

- Are the windows clean? Are all broken or damaged panes of glass replaced to maximise natural light and aid insulation?

- Do you encourage building users to save electricity i.e. turning equipment off – not leaving it on standby. Turning off lights when leaving the room. Timing meetings to minimise heating requirements.

These questions show simple but effective ways that will allow you to begin reducing your carbon footprint immediately.

5 Energy efficiency

When we look at energy efficiency, we need to look at this in two distinct areas. For convenience these will be called 'church heating' and 'other areas'.

As stated earlier, church heating is quite complex and I will go into that later. Firstly we will take a look at 'other areas' in which we can make savings.

Good management is the key to any successful operation and running a church complex is no different than running a small business. The first step in energy savings are best made by careful and practical use of the church buildings in order to make savings in light and heat.

Energy efficiency is the responsibility of everybody who uses the building. Scheduling meetings and weekday activities to minimise heating requirements and making sure everybody who uses the church is aware of the energy saving strategies in use is one way to make sure that everybody plays their part.

During the winter months, meetings held earlier in the day will make the most use of natural light, helping to reduce the need for electric lights.

Meetings that follow on from one another, held in the same room will also help to reduce the heating costs. Not only will the room have been preheated by the heating system, but also the body heat of people from the previous meeting will have reduced the heat load requirements.

Many churches now have audiovisual equipment, a fully functional office, complete with computer, printer and copier – which are usually left on standby. Many have security systems as well as an operational kitchen, all of which use vast amounts of electricity.

Making a building energy efficient means trying to reduce any wasted energy. That means not leaving electrical equipment on standby, turning off all lights when not needed. Cut out the waste!

Insulating walls and ceilings to prevent heat escaping are important issues, but only if the construction of the building permits it. In modern buildings this should not be an issue, however in some older or medieval churches you might run into architectural problems.

Energy efficiency means not paying for fuel that you don't actually need thereby reducing gas and electricity bills. That can only be a good thing in a world where energy is becoming increasingly expensive.

One thing we can all do with electrical equipment is to turn it off completely, electrical equipment with standby really should really be phased out but until it is, it is better to unplug appliances at the wall, obviously this does not apply to fridges, freezers or essential equipment.

The argument against banning equipment with standby in the UK revolves around an increase in costs to companies having to produce standby free appliances especially for the UK market and possible conflicts with EU free trade restrictions.

However at the G8 summit it was agreed to promote the International Energy Agency's initiative to reduce the standby energy requirements for all new appliances to 1 watt by the year 2010.

Turning appliances off at the wall will not only save energy as on average a computer on standby will still use almost as much power as it does when fully on, with no programmes running. Other advantages of turning off electrical equipment include increasing the lifespan of the appliance, reducing fire risks and of course saving money.

There are now products on the market that have been designed to reduce the amount of power an appliance will use by simply cutting the power to the appliance when it is not in use.

Energy saving lamps (bulbs) are a great way of saving on lighting costs and although slightly more expensive than ordinary bulbs - soon the standard incandescent lamp will be a thing of the past - they last approx 10 times longer and use just 4% of the energy so easily save you money in the long run. The cost of these lamps has rapidly come down so the change over should be relatively painless. I put them in my own home some years ago - when they were still quite expensive, but I can honestly say, I cannot remember replacing one. My energy bills have been reduced considerably over the years; mind you, this has been aided by the kids leaving home!

Solar powered outdoor lights requiring no electricity or cabling can now be brought at any D.I.Y. or gardening store. They simply stick into the ground or wall and collect energy throughout the day, once it gets dark, they light up automatically and light up paths, entrances etc very effectively. These again can be bought at reasonable prices and the choices are growing; I have now seen these on lamp standards and they are very effective for low levels of light.

Drawing thick insulating curtains over windows at night also prevents heat loss especially in old buildings where double-glazing etc cannot be used. It would be criminal to remove a stained glass window to increase insulation when other measures can be taken.

It is not only energy we should be saving but water too. Checking for leaks and fixing dripping taps is essential in old buildings and can reduce water bills. The trick is to only use what you need, that means boiling only just enough water for tea and coffee for after a service. Toilets can now be fitted with a dual flushing system to save water and a cheaper method is putting half a brick into the toilet cistern to reduce the amount of water used in each flush.

6 Heating

I will start by saying that by the time you have reached the end of this chapter you may have decided that it is wiser to call in an expert to have a full, professional survey carried out on the heating. I say this because there is a vast difference in places of worship.

There is not a universal solution to heating a church, in fact quite often what is a solution for one church, could in actual fact be a problem in another.

It is however, the area in which most savings can be made in our carbon footprint and indeed our fuel costs; in some cases these savings are quite substantial. I will try to spell them out step by step for you.

The problem is that churches are vastly different in their construction. For instance, if you have a medieval church then fabric concerns are paramount. Not only do you have to be environmentally aware of your responsibilities, you also have the added problem (or joy) of protecting what is part of this country's heritage. Protecting the fabric of the building is directly linked to the heating.

On the other hand you may have a modern church where the aesthetics are not an issue. The heating solution here will be vastly different from the medieval solution.

In order to start, I think that we need to identify the age and construction of your church, to make this a little easier I think we could probably group together all churches built in and prior to the Victorian period. Believe it or not, I think that this age of church is probably the easiest to heat.

Hands up if your church is one of these! Good.

Now does your heating system consist of large bore, cast iron pipework and radiators. It does? I am afraid that is bad news. You have a typical Victorian heating system. Sorry, but it has to go and the sooner the better.

Victorian heating systems worked on a completely different arrangement than modern systems. All Victorian systems were designed for solid fuel and as such they were designed for continuous operation and the system had a very large water content.

It needed this amount of water because the system always had to have more water in it than the boiler could heat. There was none of the time clocks, pumps or electrical controls that we now take for granted. The system would probably have run from September to Easter and kept the church at a steady 13°C.

Comfort levels would have been acceptable as the expectation of people was considerably less than it is today. Today, most of the congregation will usually travel to church from a centrally heated house in a heated car, most people no longer posses an overcoat, a far cry from the cold industrial days of the mid-Victorian period.

Many of those systems still exist today. One very important factor of a Victorian system operating today is that an extremely high water content is transferring to a relatively small heating surface. The average Victorian system – even working with a modern boiler will probably have efficiency of less than 30% and in most cases less than 20%. This did not matter at the time that they were installed as a local industrialist usually donated the fuel to the church in an effort to ease his conscience for exploiting children in his factory. Sad but true!

One statement that people often make when I visit churches with this type of system is that the system is quite efficient when it is running. I am not sure whether they say this to comfort themselves that the colossal fuel bill is actually justified, or that they actually believe it!

Believe me if you have any part of your system that is Victorian, it is NOT efficient. I have calculated that if the average parish church replaced a Victorian heating system it could reduce the carbon footprint by approximately 65%. It may seem amazing but it is true. That also equates to a similar amount of saving on your energy bill too!

Before you hurry down to the church to switch off the heating, you need to know that it is actually better for the fabric of the building to keep a background heat within the church to protect the fabric. This is very important the Church Buildings Council recommend that a background temperature of no less than 10°C/11°C should be maintained throughout the year with an occupied temperature of no more than 19/20°C

The reason for this background heat is mainly to stabilise the humidity within the church. Rapid changes in humidity can cause fabric damage, in particular to the organ, timbers and of course to plaster. The trick with a building like this is to heat it evenly and gently. The really clever bit is to do this expediently minimising your energy consumption. You must remember that rapid changes in heat give rapid changes in humidity and in this type of building it could be catastrophic.

This also means that anything that blows heat into the building has the potential to be harmful. The reason for this is that when you introduce hot air into a building above approx 45/46°C, then the curve of the air rises rapidly. Hot air systems discharge air at anything up to 80°C. The hot air goes directly to the top of the building and quickly changes the humidity and as the system is only warming the air within the church, rather than the fabric, the walls stay cold thus allowing moisture to condensate on the cold surfaces. So it is better to avoid big jet-engine type blow heaters, hot air systems and generally anything that has a fan on it.

The thing that a church of this age does have going for it is that the once you've got the building warm it is relatively easy to keep warm. This is due to the 'muscular' construction of the church. Once you apply heat to the walls of the church, the heat tends to hold within them, you are in fact turning the walls into a 'heat sink' or storage heater.

So now we know what we have to do to heat our Victorian or older type of church and protect the fabric. I cannot emphasise enough the importance of protecting the fabric of the building. If you heat the church properly, it does in fact use less energy to keep the background heat in the church, than it does to let the temperature drop and then to try and warm it back up again. The bigger, more frequently used churches tend to keep higher background temperatures. I know of two cathedrals I have heated where the background temperature is kept at 14°C and rises to around 16/18°C for worship. This works well as the walls are approx five feet thick and it makes sense to keep a higher background heat once the temperature has been attained.

If you don't protect the fabric the consequential damage is not only detrimental to the building in terms of the financial cost of the repairs but the ongoing impact those repairs will have on the environment, through the use of raw materials, manufacturing, transportation etc.

So how do we go about our task? Many churches make the mistake of replacing the boiler without first seeking expert advice. They assume that because the church is not warm enough, the existing boiler does not have the capacity to heat the building. It is usually very simple to find a local installer who will be only too pleased to supply and fit a new efficient condensing boiler. That should do the trick!

On a modern system that would probably be fine, but to be truthful, on a Victorian hot water system it won't do very much to help. It will increase the combustion efficiency which is all well and good, but it is still trying to heat up a massive water content, in a system that was originally designed over 100 years ago, to only give 13°C when running continuously for 7 days.

The problem is the water content. There is too much water with too little heating surface. You are burning fuel just to warm all of that unnecessary water, to change the efficiency you must reduce the water content and increase the heating surface.

Some years ago I visited a church in Manchester where they gave me a copy of their original heating quotation dating back to 1875. In those days they quoted for heat by the length of pipe within the church and the water content, I have used this as an illustration of how uneconomic it is in the present day.

A Parish church using a Victorian heating system with approx 700 feet of 4 inch, large bore, cast iron pipes and 8 cast iron radiators had a water content of approx 450 gallons and gave a heat output of approx 140,000 BThU's (British Thermal Unit). Excuse the 'old money' version, but for you young whippersnappers that is approximately 41 Kilowatts.

One British Thermal Unit (BThU) is the amount of heat required to raise the temperature of one pound of water by one degree Fahrenheit.

So by my calculations of basic physics to raise the church from 46ºF to 66ºF would take around 12 hours.

The heat requirements I calculate would be 450 gallons x 10 lbs per gal x 140ºF (water temp rise to affect surface temp of emitters) = 630,000 BThUs for the first two hours dropping to approx 180,000 BThUs for the next 10 hours using the typical warm up cycle of a Parish church.

In truth many churches take much longer to heat up and achieve much lower temperatures. Total energy used (output) would equal 3 million BThUs. Add to this a boiler efficiency of perhaps only 70 % and this would mean the energy burnt to achieve heat for Sunday service would be 4.7 million BThUs or about 1,380 kW hours.

As previously stated the design of this system was intended to run continuously. The heating surface of such a system is insufficient to give the comfort levels that are required today or are even sufficient to adequately protect the fabric of the building without constant operation.

If we compare this with a modern low pressure hot water system we see that by using small bore pipes and high output triple panelled radiators, the water content would be reduced to approx 60 gallons and the heating surface increased to approx 400,000 BThUs. This would result in a warm up time of 2 – 3 hours as opposed to in excess of 12.

The energy would then be used to bring the church to a higher, more comfortable level and would be reduced to approx 1.2 million BThUs (approx 350kW per hour) over a 3 hour period.

Coupled with a condensing boiler burning gas at an average of 97% efficiency this would mean a total burn of approx 1.23 million BThUs or approx 360KW hours. This would result in a saving of fuel consumed by a staggering 74%. Also as condensing boilers have low Nox emissions the carbon savings are even greater.

These calculations are rudimentary - please forgive me if they are a few percent out and are only provided as an example of the gross inefficiency some systems are operating at. If there are any retired professors out there with spare time available then I am sure you could give me a more definitive calculation.

It makes sense that if these problems are addressed they will do far more for the environment than simply trying to add on renewable energy sources to an inefficient system.

So the golden rules for heating churches built in the Victorian period or older are:

- Keep the water content to a minimum
- Keep as many of the heat emitters on the external walls as possible.
- Avoid using fan assistance wherever and whenever possible
- Ensure that the system is under proper control.

We will cover controls and fuel selection in more depth a little later.

I think by now you have got the idea of how heating should be approached in a 'muscular' church and the reasoning behind it. I chose Victorian in particular because it was a period of our history that redefined our country as well as our churches.

At the beginning of the Victorian era almost 80% of the country worked on the land, at the end of the period over 80% worked in industry. Interestingly although the Victorians built over 4000 churches consecrating on average more than two churches a week, they also refurbished another 7000, although there are many that would say they vandalised an awful lot! Personally I think they were prolific engineers and I have a great love of gothic architecture. I bet you don't know of any Victorian church that need air conditioning do you? Just think how much energy could be saved if we were to apply similar principals in designs today.

At the end of the Victorian period or shortly afterward, the building of churches slowed down but those that were built were generally built to similar standards until around the time of the Second World War. So realistically if your church were built before then the same principles of heating would apply.

The real problem in heating churches comes for those that were built during the sixties and seventies, also in some cases the early eighties. This was a bad time for anything to be built. Companies were experimenting with new building methods and general construction standards were of a poor quality. Strangely there was a glut of new churches built throughout the country during this period.

I know from personal experience that the Catholic diocese of both Liverpool and Salford had a big building programme.

I could never understand why so many churches had electric heating installed. Many of them were under-floor heating systems that were grossly inefficient with a short life span as the buildings were built on a concrete raft which usually cracked and split after a couple of years, taking the heating element with it. Then I stumbled across a Government article written in 1954 that said that electricity would become so cheap it would not be worth metering. How wrong can you be!

The first thing you need to do with this type of church is to make it as air tight as possible without suffocating the congregation. A building of this age usually has no heat retaining properties, so the principal of warming the fabric of the building we applied to the Victorian church will definitely not work here. In this type of church we can look at warming the air within the church and we can also look at rapid warm-up solutions. The reason that we can do this is because our modern church is built from pre-stressed materials and any rapid changes in temperature or humidity should not damage the fabric. Also in this type of building we do not need to keep a steady background temperature, in most cases mere frost protection will suffice. Warm air systems can sometimes suit a building like this very well.

We do however; need to ensure that we cut out all the areas where heat could escape from the church.

- Check that you have a good thickness of loft insulation.

- Double-glazing in this type of building is a must.

- Make sure that doors have automatic closing devices to prevent them from being left open thereby cutting down on draughts.

Heat emitters could have fans fitted, but remember that they are an added maintenance factor and they can become very noisy with age. If you have a number of smaller rooms, make sure that you have independent thermostats on the radiators to keep the room under control.

Another good way of reducing energy in a church is to fit high level de-stratification fans. In churches built during the sixties there tended to be an unusually high glass content and many had high or irregular roof lines. These tend to trap heat and stop it circulating. Slow running 'Punka' type fans can act to lower the 'heat ceiling' which will have a significant effect on your energy use. A word of caution though, if you are about to fit high level fans, ensure that they are above the line of incoming light. If not they could give a strobe effect, which is not good for the congregation, or the celebrant.

Churches built after the mid eighties tend to have been constructed to higher standards, i.e. with double-glazing and adequate loft insulation, however now is the time to go and check it out.

Leaky lofts cost energy and we need to be all about saving energy. Don't forget, all these actions are actually saving you money. Good isn't it?

Now we will shift our attention to controls. You could have the best heating system in the country, but if it isn't under proper control then it will be costing you and costing the environment.

First of all we have to ask who is responsible for ensuring that the heating is switched on or off for services. This brings us to proper management but you would be amazed at how many churches set a clock in September and never look at it again throughout the season, or indeed don't have anybody who takes responsibility for it.

A proper control system should be intelligent or optimising, that is it should be maximising fuel efficiency by monitoring the inside and outside temperatures so that it does not waste energy. If you have a large complex, the system should be capable of being controlled in different zones so that heating operation is restricted to the areas of demand. This means that if you have three separate areas then the controls should reflect that and allow you to have independent heat and time control in each of those areas. Typically the controller should allow for three or four time settings on each zone, for each day of the week. Electronic controllers are relatively cheap these days, so good control comes relatively inexpensively.

Ideally your controller should have a code entry to prevent tampering by unauthorised users. Every church has someone who likes to 'play' with things - we all know that. I bet you are thinking of them now aren't you? If you can't get code entry, although they are readily available, then put it in a lockable box, with a big 'KEEP OUT' sign on it. The main thing is that only one or two people should have access to this and they should take responsibility for the operation of the heating. Trust me this will reduce your fuel consumption.

6.1 Fuel

Fuel selection can vary due to local forces and indeed personal views, particularly when we discuss renewable energies. I think for now we will leave renewable energy and concentrate on the fossil fuels. There is more on renewable energy later on.

It seems that almost every day when you pick up the newspaper that cost of fuel has risen again. At the time of writing this, I have just returned from America where they are incensed at the cost of filling up their gas guzzling cars, it cost me all of £16 to fill my hire car. This morning I filled my own car up here in England and it cost me almost £90! However, most of that was tax and though I could spout on for pages with a political rant about taxes, I will resist the urge and save that for another day.

It does however highlight the point that costs escalate quite rapidly and it is hard to give accurate information in these fuel volatile times.

When I first started in the heating business it cost £25.00 for 500 gallons (2270 litres) of heating oil, with prices like that it was hardly surprising that efficiency was not at the top of the agenda. Today that full tank would cost over £1300.00!

As I travel the country visiting churches and looking at the heating systems, I am often told by clients that they want to change from oil to gas as they have been told it is more efficient. In most cases that is probably true. You will be increasing your combustion efficiency to approx 96% from approx 75%. It certainly is cheaper to buy gas at the moment, but as I have already explained, it does not mean that you will be making large energy savings. Putting a brand new condensing gas boiler onto a Victorian heating system will do very little to reduce your carbon footprint. You have to ensure that you are transferring that energy from your boiler to your church in an efficient way and that is by keeping the water content to a minimum whilst maximising the radiated heat output

So how do fuel costs compare? I have always tried to keep up to date on fuel costs, but the market can be a very confusing place with its rapidly changing prices. Once upon a time, gas was always measured in Therms or British Thermal Units (BThUs). Call me old-fashioned but I still use this as a unit for my calculations, I find it easier to think in these terms.

Some years ago they changed the way they measured and sold gas to kilowatt hours (kW/hrs) to give it some sort of parity to electricity. I remember, years ago when you bought a gas fire or a boiler, the manufacturer would display the gas input in BThUs and the output in kW.

To my mind this was to disguise the gross inefficiency of the appliances. A typical gas fire would be less than 55% efficient.

When we come to oil, the measurement has changed from gallons to litres, but oil boiler manufacturers would quote the burning rate of the boiler in U.S. gallons per hour and a U.S. gallon as you may already know is smaller than an imperial gallon. An imperial gallon is 20 ounces compared with 16 in a U.S gallon.

Propane it is even more confusing as you can buy that in either litres or kilograms with the output quoted in kilowatts!

To further add to the confusion although we all tend to use kilowatts as a unit of heat measurement in the U.K. many European boiler manufacturers use Calories and Joules as outputs.

I said it was confusing and to the uninitiated it certainly is. You also have to factor in the efficiency of the appliance and this is all before you have transferred the heat to the heating system in church.

I have put together a table of comparative fuel costs assuming identical heating systems after the boiler. These costs take into account the efficiency of modern appliances. For example, electricity is arguably 100% efficient, all the inefficiency has been factored out before it reaches you. Gas condensing boilers have efficiencies of approx 96%, as do propane boilers. Oil boilers are slightly below that at approx 93%.

In this table I have factored these in to give a price for a kW/hr of each of these fuels.

Oil – figures based on a burning rate of oil through a condensing boiler.			
50KWoil	=	5.56 litres of oil	
1KW oil	=	0.111 litres	
Price per litre		Cost per KW hour (in pence)	
70	=	7.77	
65	=	7.21	
60	=	6.66	
55	=	6.10	
50	=	5.55	
45	=	4.99	
40	=	4.44	
Propane – Figures based on condensing boiler by a leading manufacturer			
	60KW/hr	=	10 litres per hour
	80kW/hr	=	13 litres per hour
1 KW propane = 0.166 litres			
Price per litre		Cost per KW hour (in pence)	
70	=	11.66	
65	=	10.83	
60	=	9.99	
55	=	9.16	
50	=	8.33	
45	=	7.49	
40	=	6.66	
Gas			
Average National Rate	=	2.85p per KW Hour	
Electricity			
Off Peak	=	4.50p per KW hour (Average 5.5p ph)	
Standard Rate	=	11p per KW hour (Best Average)	

As you can see the cost of gas at a base rate is by far the cheapest to buy, gas is also delivered 'on tap' with no storage needed. Unfortunately not everyone has a gas supply available.

Most modern boilers have low Nox emissions, which means that they produce lower amounts of carbon dioxide. You will see the words 'low Nox' attached to many new boilers and it means that it reduces all the oxides of nitrogen.

If gas is not available then oil is usually then next choice, but finding a site for fuel storage can be a problem in some churches. The added benefit of an oil-fired boiler is that it can burn bio-fuel with only very minimal adjustment.

The attraction of electricity to some is the clean burn with no emissions; you must remember however that most electricity at source has had emissions as part of the production process. When wind power and hydro-electricity production along with other renewable energy sources become more prevalent, then these will of course be reduced.

Electricity at base cost is some 350% more expensive than gas. It does offer good off-peak choices if the right tariff can be agreed with your supplier and the off-peak times can fit in quite well with church timetables.

6.2 Boilers

I have mentioned 'condensing' boilers in previous pages and for the none-technical among you perhaps I should explain the difference between a condensing boiler and a conventional boiler.

A flame that is created by a mixture of fuel and air heats a conventional boiler. The heat from the flame then heats the heat exchanger (the part that holds the water) and the residual heat passes into the flue and is discharged to the atmosphere. A conventional boiler cannot have efficiency greater than 80% as in order to get that it would need to take so much heat out of the products of combustion that water would form.

A condensing boiler has additional or supplementary heat exchange pass, which takes heat and forms a trap to collect the water vapour, or condensation. This is then drained away from the boiler as a waste product. Condensing boilers can produce an average of around 96% gross efficiency. That is to say, if you have a modern efficient system with a conventional boiler, switching to a condensing boiler could make an instant saving of around 20% on your fuel bills and of course reduce your carbon emissions.

A lot of people think that their heating system is efficient because the radiators get really hot, without fully thinking it through. A lot mistakenly think that if they replace the boiler to a more efficient condensing boiler then they have an efficient system, well as you know by now, this is not always the case.

It is wise to take expert advice before replacing the boiler. Most dioceses now have a heating advisor who will come along and give his time freely. If you go to a commercial organisation or company, make sure they know what they are doing; heating a church is not like heating a house or an office block. Take expert advice from someone with a lot of church experience and even if you have to pay for it, you can be sure that it will be cheaper in the long run. If you replace the boiler alone, make sure that it is compatible with the existing heating system and with any future plans you may have.

Your new boiler should have low Nox emissions, it should be fully condensing and it should be under proper control. A lot of boilers now have integral intelligent controls. Make sure that the controls are user friendly. A lot of modern controls take account for external temperature and weather conditions, which in a modern church complex is commendable, however if you have a Victorian or medieval church, then in my opinion they are little better than useless. External temperature weighting in this type of building can be wasteful on fuel.

You also need to be aware that boiler compartments are usually better than using the existing boiler house. A lot of Victorian boiler houses are damp, poorly ventilated and tend to have flue problems. A modern condensing boiler can usually be fitted at high-level, on a wall and have a very small flue aperture.

6.3 Other Forms of Heating

What I have talked about so far on church heating has been all about water based systems and in particular how they relate to typical parish churches - if there is such a thing. But there are many other types of systems out there.

Balanced flue

A fairly popular way of heating church buildings, particularly more modern buildings is with gas-fired balanced flued heaters. This is a system of independent heaters either sited individually in smaller church rooms or collectively in larger areas. They are popular in modern buildings because they are cheaper to install than a traditional water based system and they have a more rapid warm-up time. In a modern building this is acceptable as there are no aesthetic problems or concerns about the church fabric as modern churches are generally built from pre-stressed materials, unlike our Victorian or medieval churches.

The older type of unit had efficiencies of less than 60% but now more modern power-flued units have efficiencies in excess of 85%.

However when we choose a new heating system there are many factors to look at, particularly in terms of our green credentials. This type of unit generally has a much shorter life than a traditional system. The average life expectancy of this type of heater is somewhere between 12 and 20 years, although in some cases I have known the heaters last less than five years but that was unusual.

You also need to consider that with multi-unit installations the on-going maintenance costs can be very costly, which in itself is yet another drain on resources.

Warm Air

If your church has no fabric problems or considerations then warm air could be an option. Warm air is ideal for a quick warm up, this may allow you to operate the system for a shorter period of time but may result in condensation within the building. Warm air systems can be intrusive as the fans move air at a high velocity, which can feel uncomfortable as well as producing noise.

Electric

There are some circumstances where electric options come to the fore. For instance you may have a traditional heating system for the main worship area, but have a need for a half hour service in the Lady Chapel. Clearly in these circumstances you would want to use an alternative to conserve energy.

I did say at the beginning, that the section on heating was complex; I hope that I have helped clarify things a little. I think the most important thing to say is, don't be afraid to ask for help, this is a very specialised field and it is very important to get it right.

If you are intending to change anything on your heating system you need to get it right. Make the savings really count and do not just appear to be paying lip service to the green issues.

I recently stayed in a hotel that had a sticker on the bathroom wall – as most hotels do - asking guests to save the planet by re-using towels for the duration of the stay; a perfectly reasonable request and something I am happy to comply with. The irony of it was that for the entire length of my five-night stay, the electric towel rail was heated constantly night and day! Further to that, there was not even a switch to allow guests to turn it off!

7 Renewable Energies

As we have already established no two churches are the same. There is a large difference in size, age, aesthetics and construction. We have already learned that you can not have a 'one size fits all' approach to heating a church and this is even more pronounced when we look at renewable solutions.

I have to say from the very start of this chapter that if you have one of our typical Victorian parish churches, that renewable energy may be a dream you are unable to deliver, particularly if your church is listed.

If you have a modern church, then renewable energy is much more accessible. If you are looking at an entirely new building, then the options are excellent. You could be virtually carbon neutral and totally efficient in all your 'green areas'

We need to go through the main renewable energy options, looking at the pros and cons of each system and try to relate them to your own church application.

I have tried to keep things simple but until you try to explain things in a measured way you don't realise just how complicated descriptions can be. I apologise if some of the following is a little confusing but I am trying to be as thorough as possible

7.1 Solar

Solar energy is energy from the sun in the form of radiated heat and light. It drives the climate, the weather and it supports life on Earth. Solar energy technologies make controlled use of this energy resource.

Solar power refers specifically to the conversion of sunlight into electricity by photovoltaic [1], concentrating solar thermal devices or various experimental technologies.

In building design, thermal mass is used to conserve heat and lighting techniques optimize light. Solar water heaters heat swimming pools and provide domestic hot water.

In agriculture, greenhouses grow specialty crops and photovoltaic[1]-powered pumps bring water to grazing animals. Evaporation ponds find applications in the commercial and industrial sectors where they are used to harvest salt and clean waste streams of contaminants.

Solar distillation and disinfection techniques produce potable water for millions of people worldwide. Family size solar cookers and larger solar kitchens concentrate sunlight for cooking, drying and pasteurization.

More sophisticated concentrating technologies magnify the rays of the sun for high temperature material testing, metal smelting and industrial chemical production. A range of prototype solar vehicles provide ground, air and sea transportation.

Solar energy technologies utilize solar radiation for practical ends. Technologies that utilize secondary solar resources such as biomass, wind, waves and ocean thermal gradients can be included in a broader description of solar energy but only primary resource applications are discussed here. The qualities and performance of solar technologies vary widely between regions; therefore, solar technologies should be used in a way that carefully considers these variations.

Solar hot water systems use sunlight to heat water. Commercial solar water heaters began appearing in the United States in the 1890's. These systems saw increasing use until the 1920's but were gradually replaced by relatively cheap and more reliable conventional heating fuels. Here in the UK the use of solar panels is a relatively new technology.

Solar water heating technologies have high efficiencies relative to other solar technologies. Performance will depend upon the site of deployment, but flat-plate and evacuated-tube collectors will deliver water temperatures of 20°C -120°C and can be expected to have efficiencies above 60% during normal operating conditions.

The most common types of solar water heaters are:

- Batch systems
- Flat plate collectors
- Evacuated tube collectors.

Common applications include heating swimming pools, domestic hot water, space heating and thermal storage.

Electricity can be generated from the sun in several ways. Photovoltaic (PV) has been mainly developed for small and medium-sized applications, from the calculator powered by a single solar cell to the PV power plant. For large-scale generation, concentrating solar thermal power plants have been more common but new multi-megawatt PV plants have been built recently. Other solar electrical generation technologies are still at the experimental stage.

Storage is an important issue in the development of solar energy as modern energy systems usually assume continuous availability of energy. Solar energy is not available at night and the performance of solar power systems is affected by unpredictable weather patterns so a storage medium or back-up power system must be used.

Thermal mass systems can store solar energy in the form of heat at useful temperatures for domestic use with daily or seasonal durations. Thermal storage systems generally use readily available materials with high specific heat capacities such as water, earth and stone. Well designed systems can lower peak demand for conventional energy sources when used in tandem and can shift the time of use to off-peak hours.

Photovoltaic Cells

Solar cells convert energy from the sun directly into electricity by what is known as the photovoltaic effect. Edmund Becquerel first noticed this in 1839, when he saw that as light was directed to the electrodes of a battery cell increased the voltage. This led to the development of photocells, which were used light sensors. It was not until much later that devices with a performance good enough for electrical power generation came on the scene. In 1954 a team at Bell Laboratories reported that they had made a solar cell with a conversion efficiency of 6%. As Solar cells were a light, reliable source of power, they were soon used in space programmes. Vanguard I was the first satellite to be powered by solar energy and was launched in 1958. As they have a record of reliability solar cells have been used as the main source of power for satellites. Conversion efficiencies have increased to over 24% and power levels from a few milliwatts to tens of kilowatts. The massive increase of oil prices by OPEC in 1973 caused interest to grow in the possibility of using solar power closer to home.

Photovoltaic (PV) technology is now a growing industry with a wide range of everyday uses; powering calculators and some novelties. These days with advances in integrated circuits and low-power LCD it is less common to see solar powered calculators, but on the other-hand there has been an increase in items such as parking meters or temporary traffic signs making use of solar power.

Mass produced pv cells only have an efficiency of approx 10%. This means that to produce electricity this way can be more expensive than producing it other ways.

When used in existing distribution grids. It incurs an energy loss of 4 - 12%.

Solar cells produce DC (direct current) which must be converted to AC (alternating current) before it can be used.

Solar power is not available at night and is less available in cloudy weather condition, so a method of storage has to be found.

Clearly these cells can have a use within a church complex, perhaps with external lighting for footpaths, gardens etc, but not within the realms of heating. A new build church could have low voltage lighting installed at the design stage and make use of hot water warmed by solar panels.

Rechargeable batteries can be used to store excess electricity from a PV system. Lead acid batteries are the most common type of battery associated with PV systems as they are relatively cheap and easily available. Batteries used in off-grid applications should be sized for three to five days of capacity and should limit depth of discharge to 50% to minimize cycling and prolong battery life.

Excess electricity can also be fed into the transmission grid to meet electrical demands elsewhere. Net metering programs give PV system owners credit for the electricity they deliver to the grid. This credit is used to offset electricity provided from the grid when the PV system cannot meet demand.

Water-based Solar Panels

In Great Britain each square metre of a south-facing roof receives around 1000kWh of solar radiation each year. This means that the roof of many homes will receive more than enough energy from the sun in a year to provide both the space heating and hot water. By using solar collectors it is possible to capture some of this solar radiation and reduce the consumption of fossil fuels like gas, coal and oil.

The sun is used to provide domestic hot water in many countries. In Great Britain it is possible to use the sun to provide most of the hot water requirements for an 'average' family from about May to September. It is also possible to obtain some 'pre-heating' of the cold water supply during the other months.

In principle it is possible to scale up the size of a solar water heater to provide central heating but in general this is not cost effective. However, a solar water heater could be used in a pre-heating arrangement if the produced hot water were not used elsewhere. Hot water is normally produced by heating cold mains water to the required temperature with a gas or oil fired boiler or an immersion heater. By slightly modifying the conventional heating system, solar collectors could be introduced.

The principle of water heating panels is to collect heat in the form of hot water and then transfer it to an internal 'holding' cylinder. In an ideal scenario this would then operate in tandem with a highly efficient condensing boiler, heating the church using a conventional type hot water system.

Within church use this does have a potential problem as the water would still have to be circulated in summer in order to dissipate the heat from the panels. With little or no demand for domestic hot water the panels would over-heat and destroy themselves. For purely domestic hot water this would be ideal, but for heating a typical Victorian Church it would not be suitable. This is particularly frustrating as almost every Victorian church I know has a large south facing roof area.

Another major problem with this type of building is that any work carried out would have to have all the relevant permissions, i.e. a Church of England church would be required to go through the faculty process and, if the building were a listed one then permission from English Heritage and possibly the Victorian Society may have to be sought. This could prove difficult if the major south facing roof is in a very visible location. As well as being a good steward of the environment, you also have to be a good steward of our heritage.

If you have a modern complex with demand for hot water then this type of unit would have a use. If you chose this option then it is paramount that the units are correctly sized to give the correct output.

Roof space is usually easy to find though the units can be mounted at floor level. They are relatively easy to make for the D.I.Y enthusiast but I really would not recommend it in a church location.

7.2 Heat Pumps

According to the second law of thermodynamics, heat cannot spontaneously flow from a colder location to a hotter area; work is required to achieve this. Heat pumps differ in how they apply this work to move heat, but they can essentially be thought of as heat engines operating in reverse. A heat engine allows energy to flow from a hot 'source' to a cold heat 'sink'. Conversely, a heat pump requires work to move thermal energy from a cold source to a warmer heat sink.

Since the heat pump uses a certain amount of work to move the heat, the amount of energy deposited at the hot side is greater than the energy taken from the cold side by an amount equal to the work required. Conversely, for a heat engine, the amount of energy taken from the hot side is greater than the amount of energy deposited in the cold heat sink since some of the heat has been converted to work.

One common type of heat pump works by exploiting the physical properties of an evaporating and condensing fluid known as a refrigerant.

The working fluid in its gaseous state, is pressurized and circulated through the system by a compressor.

On the discharge side of the compressor, the now hot and highly pressurized gas is cooled in a heat exchanger called a condenser until it condenses into a high pressure, moderate temperature liquid.

The condensed refrigerant then passes through a pressure-lowering device like an expansion valve, capillary tube, or possibly a work-extracting device such as a turbine. This device then passes the low pressure, barely liquid (saturated vapor) refrigerant to another heat exchanger, the evaporator where the refrigerant evaporates into a gas via heat absorption. The refrigerant then returns to the compressor and the cycle is repeated.

In such a system it is essential that the refrigerant reaches a sufficiently high temperature when compressed, since the second law of thermodynamics prevents heat from flowing from a cold fluid to a hot heat sink. Similarly, the fluid must reach a sufficiently low temperature when allowed to expand or heat cannot flow from the cold region into the fluid. In particular, the pressure difference must be great enough for the fluid to condense at the hot side and still evaporate in the lower pressure region at the cold side. The greater the temperature difference, the greater the required pressure difference and consequently more energy is needed to compress the fluid. Thus as with all heat pumps, the energy efficiency (amount of heat moved per unit of input work required) decreases with increasing temperature difference.

Due to the variations required in temperatures and pressures, many different refrigerants are available. Refrigerators, air conditioners and some heating systems are common applications that use this technology.

In commercial heating and air conditioning applications, a heat pump normally refers to a vapor-compression refrigeration device that includes a reversing valve and optimized heat exchangers, so that the direction of heat flow may be reversed. The reversing valve switches the direction of refrigerant through the cycle and therefore the heat pump may deliver either heating or cooling to a building. In the cooler climates the default setting of the reversing valve is heating. The default setting in warmer climates is cooling. As the two heat exchangers - the condenser and evaporator, must swap functions, they are optimized to perform adequately in both modes. As such, the efficiency of a reversible heat pump is typically slightly less than two separately optimized machines.

In plumbing applications, a heat pump is sometimes used to heat or preheat water for swimming pools or domestic water heaters.

In somewhat rare applications, both the heat extraction and addition capabilities of a single heat pump can be useful and typically results in very effective use of the input energy. For example, when an air cooling need can be matched to a water heating load, a single heat pump can serve two useful purposes. Unfortunately, these situations are rare because the demand profiles for heating and cooling are often significantly different.

Most commonly, heat pumps draw heat from the air (outside or inside air) or from the ground. The heat drawn from the ground is in most cases stored solar heat and it should not be confused with geothermal heat, though the latter will contribute in some small measure to all heat in the ground. Other heat sources include water; nearby streams and other natural water bodies have been used and sometimes domestic waste water which is often warmer than the ambient temperature.

7.3 Geothermal

In recent years, the term geothermal heating has frequently been used to refer to the heating that can be achieved through the use of a geothermal heat pump. This technique is generally for residential use because the heat demands of a residential property are far less than those required for a church.

A refrigerant liquid is pumped through pipes in the ground, heating the liquid. This liquid then is brought back into the property and the heat exchanged. The same technique is used to cool the property.

Geothermal heat pumps take advantage of the natural constant temperature of the earth. During winter when the ground temperature is warmer than the air above it, geothermal heat pumps use the earth's soil (or groundwater) to recover heat from the earth.

During summer months, geothermal heat pumps deliver heat to the same relatively cool soil (or groundwater) rather than delivering it to the hot outside air. As a result, the heat is pumped over a smaller temperature difference with a geothermal heat pump and this leads to higher efficiency and lower energy use.

The most common system is a closed loop system; this type of system circulates the fluid through the loop fields' pipes and does not pull in water from a water source. In a closed loop system there is no direct interaction between the fluid and the earth; only heat transfer across the pipe. The length of vertical or horizontal loop required is a function of the ground formation thermal conductivity, ground temperatureand heating and cooling power needed, it also depends on the balance between the amount of heat rejected to and absorbed from the ground during the course of the year. A rough approximation of the soil temperature is the average daily temperature for the region. Although copper and other metals can be used, polythene seems to be the most common tubing material used currently by installers; often 3/4 inches (19mm) inside diameter tubing.

There are four common types of closed loop systems:

- Vertical,
- Horizontal
- Slinky[1]
- Pond

Vertical Closed Loop Field

A vertical closed loop field is composed of pipes that run vertically in the ground. A hole is bored in the ground, typically, 150 - 250 feet deep (45–75m).

Pipe pairs in the hole are joined with a U-shaped cross connector at the bottom of the hole. The bore-hole is commonly filled with a bentonite grout surrounding the pipe to provide a good thermal connection to the surrounding soil or rock to maximize the heat transfer.

Vertical loop fields are typically used when there is a limited square footage of land available. Bore holes are spaced 5–6 m apart and are generally 15m (50ft) deep per kW of cooling. During the cooling season, the local temperature rise in the bore field is influenced most by the moisture travel in the soil. Reliable heat transfer models have been developed through sample bore holes.

Horizontal Closed Loop Field

A horizontal closed loop field is composed of pipes that run horizontally in the ground. A long horizontal trench, deeper than the frost line, is dug and U-shaped coils are placed horizontally inside the same trench. A trench for a horizontal loop field will be similar to one seen under the slinky loop field; however, the width strictly depends on how many loops are installed. Horizontal loop fields are very common and economical if there is adequate land available.

Slinky Closed Loop Field

A slinky closed loop field is installed in the horizontal orientation; however, the pipes overlay each other. The easiest way of picturing a slinky field is to imagine holding a slinky (a coil shaped toy) on the top and bottom with your hands and then move your hands in opposite directions. A slinky loop field is used if there is not adequate room for a true horizontal system, but it still allows for an easy installation.

Closed Pond Loop

A closed pond loop is not as common, but is becoming increasingly popular. A pond loop is achieved by placing coils of pipe at the bottom of an appropriately sized pond or water source. This system has been promoted in the United States by the DNR (Department of Natural Resources), who support geothermal systems and the use of ponds for geothermal systems.

Open loop systems

In contrast to the closed loop systems, an open loop system pulls water directly from a well, lake, or pond. Water is pumped from one of these sources into the heat pump, where heat is either extracted or added. The water is then pumped back into a second well or source of water.

There are three general types of systems:

- Water can be pumped from a vertical water well and returned to a nearby pond.

- Water can be pumped from a body of water and returned to the same body of water.

- Water can be pumped from a vertical well and then returned to the same well.

While thermal contamination (where the ground temperature is affected by the operation of the system) is possible with any geothermal system, with proper design, planning and installation; any loop configuration can work very well for a very long time.

Open loop systems using ground water are usually much more efficient than closed systems because they will be heat exchanging with water always at ground temperature. Closed loop systems, in comparison, have to make do with the inefficient heat-transfer between the water flowing through the tubing and the ground temperature.

One of the benefits of an open loop system is that for most configurations (depending on the local environment) you are dealing with ground water at a constant temperature of approx 50°F or 10°C.

In closed loop systems the temperature of the water coming in from the loop is often within 10°F or 6°C of the temperature of the water entering the loop showing how little heat was exchanged.

The constant ground water temperatures significantly improve heat pump efficiency.

When we look at these applications in your average church they require a large surface area to collect heat from, the ground based heat pumps require digging up a large areas of land to bury the pipes. This fact alone causes problems in most churches as burials have often taken place within churchyards.

Again it has to be said that these applications could work wonderfully well on a new build project, but would cause major concerns on existing properties. However, imagine a new car park next to your church with a closed loop geothermal configuration underneath; transferring heat into a heat sink in the church floor. This would make a significant contribution to the heating of the church.

7.4 Wind Technology

Wind power is the conversion of wind energy into a useful form, such as electricity, using wind turbines. In a windmill, wind energy is directly used to crush grain or to pump water. Although wind currently produces about 1% of world-wide electricity use, it accounts for approximately 19% of electricity production in Denmark, 9% in Spain and Portugal and 6% in Germany.

Since wind speed is not constant, the annual energy production of a wind farm is never as much as the sum of the generators nominal capacity ratings multiplied by the total hours in a year.

The ratio of actual productivity in a year to this theoretical maximum is called the capacity factor. Typical capacity factors are 20-40%, with values at the upper end of the range in particularly favourable sites.

Unlike fueled generating plants, the capacity factor is limited by the inherent properties of wind. Capacity factors of other types of power plant are based mostly on fuel cost, with a small amount of downtime for maintenance. Nuclear plants have low incremental fuel costand so are run at full output and achieve a 90% capacity factor and generating plants with higher fuel cost are throttled back to follow the required load. Gas turbine plants using natural gas as fuel may be very expensive to operate and may be run only to meet peak power demand. A gas turbine plant may have an annual capacity factor of around 5-25% due to relatively high energy production cost.

Small wind generation systems with capacities of 100 kW or less are usually used to power homes, farms and small businesses. However 100kW would also be sufficient for an 'average' church. Isolated communities that otherwise rely on diesel generators may use wind turbines to displace diesel fuel consumption. Individuals purchase these systems to reduce or eliminate their electricity bills, or simply to generate their own clean power.

In urban locations, where it is difficult to obtain predictable or large amounts of wind energy, smaller systems may still be used to run low power equipment. Equipment such as parking meters or wireless internet gateways may be powered by a wind turbine that charges a small battery, replacing the need for a connection to the power grid. You may have seen these at the side of the road illuminating speed signs and the like. I have noticed a lot of this type in motorway road works for the illuminated signage.

Wind power is produced in large scale connected to electrical grids, as well as in individual turbines for providing electricity to isolated locations. I know from personal experience the visual impact these units have. They have just completed a very large wind farm on the hills above where I live. These windmills are enormous and I can understand the concern that people have about the location of these farms. However wind will be with us forever and we do need to harness as much natural energy as possible.

Wind energy is plentiful, renewable, widely distributed, clean and reduces greenhouse gas emissions when it displaces fossil-fuel derived electricity. The intermittency of wind seldom creates insurmountable problems when using it to supply a low proportion of total demand; but it presents extra costs when wind is to be used for a large fraction of demand.

As they become increasingly popular there is a lot of debate about the positioning of large wind farms, however a single small propeller can generate a fair amount of energy - especially in windy Great Britain if situated in the correct position. It still will not produce enough energy to heat a church, but it could make a significant contribution.

Planning permission would be needed and in urban areas, careful consideration needs to be paid to others who may be affected. Most urban areas do not have the wind speed necessary to produce power due to other buildings etc, so wind turbines may not really be feasible for the vast majority of churches. Currently in Scotland 90% of applications for wind farm and turbine applications are accepted, here in England only 50% of applications are accepted but time changes viewpoints and I can see more applications in England being accepted.

Perhaps the church of the future might incorporate a turbine on the tower! Well why not? I know that thought might send shivers down the spine of a few people, but it would be very practical. I am sure some budding young architect will be considering this possibility right now.

7.5 Biomass

Biomass refers to living and recently dead biological material that can be used as fuel or for industrial or commercial production. Most commonly, biomass refers to plant matter grown for use as biofuel, but it also includes plant or animal matter used for production of fibres, chemicals or heat. Biomass may also include biodegradable wastes that can be burnt as fuel. It excludes organic material which has been transformed by geological processes into substances such as coal or petroleum.

Biomass is grown from several plants, including miscanthus, switchgrass, hemp, corn, poplar, willow, sugarcane and oil palm (palm oil). The particular plant used is usually not very important to the end products, but it does affect the processing of the raw material. Production of biomass is a growing industry as interest in sustainable fuel sources is growing

Although fossil fuels have their origin in ancient biomass, they are not considered biomass by the generally accepted definition as they contain carbon that has been "out" of the carbon cycle for a very long time. Their combustion therefore disturbs the carbon dioxide content in the atmosphere.

Plastics made from biomass, like some recently developed to dissolve in seawater, are made the same way as petroleum based plastics. They are actually cheaper to manufacture and meet or exceed most performance standards but they lack the same water resistance

Biomass is part of the carbon cycle. Carbon from the atmosphere is converted into biological matter by photosynthesis. On death or combustion the carbon goes back into the atmosphere as carbon dioxide (CO_2). This happens over a relatively short timescale and plant matter used as a fuel can be constantly replaced by planting for new growth. Therefore a reasonably stable level of atmospheric carbon results from its use as a fuel. It is commonly accepted that the amount of carbon stored in dry wood is approximately 50% by weight

Though biomass is a renewable fuel and is sometimes called a "carbon neutral" fuel, its use can still contribute to global warming. This happens when the natural carbon equilibrium is disturbed; for example by deforestation or urbanization of green sites. When biomass is used as a fuel, as a replacement for fossil fuels, it still puts the same amount of CO_2 into the atmosphere.

However, when biomass is used for energy production it is widely considered carbon neutral, or a net reducer of greenhouse gasses because of the offset of methane that would have otherwise entered the atmosphere. The carbon in biomass material, which makes up approximately fifty percent of its dry-matter content, is already part of the atmospheric carbon cycle. Biomass absorbs CO_2 from the atmosphere during its growing lifetime. After its life, the carbon in biomass recycles to the atmosphere as a mixture of CO_2 and methane (CH_4), depending on the ultimate fate of the biomass material. CH_4 converts to CO_2 in the atmosphere, completing the cycle.

In contrast to biomass carbon, the carbon in fossil fuels is locked away in geological storage forever, unless extracted. The use of fossil fuels removes carbon from long-term storage and adds it to the stock of carbon in the atmospheric cycle.

Energy produced from biomass residues displaces the production of an equivalent amount of energy from fossil fuels, leaving the fossil carbon in storage.

It also shifts the composition of the recycled carbon emissions associated with the disposal of the biomass residues from a mixture of CO_2 and CH_4, to almost exclusively CO_2. In the absence of energy production applications, biomass residue carbon would be recycled to the atmosphere through some combination of rotting (biodegradation) and opening burning. Rotting produces a mixture of up to fifty percent CH_4, while open burning produces five to ten percent CH_4. Controlled combustion in a power plant converts virtually all of the carbon in the biomass to CO_2.

As CH_4 is a much stronger greenhouse gas than CO_2, shifting CH_4 emissions to CO_2 by converting biomass residues to energy significantly reduces the greenhouse warming potential of the recycled carbon associated with other fates or disposal of the biomass residues.

The avoided CH_4 emissions associated with biomass energy production have a greenhouse warming potential that is more than 20 times greater than that of the avoided fossil-fuel CO_2 emissions. Biomass power production is at least five times more effective in reducing greenhouse gas emissions than any other greenhouse gas neutral power-production technology, such as other renewable energies and nuclear.

How can we use biomass for the church?

We probably already use composting; which is a smaller, more common scale use of biomass, but large scale it could be used as a fuel to convert to heat or electricity. Wood burning boilers or bio diesel boilers are now available in capacities that would suit your church.

Wood pellet burning boilers

Like most bio fuels wood is carbon neutral, as it releases the same amount of carbon when it is burned as it absorbed during the life of the tree. Sourcing from a sustainable, managed forest can increase the environmental friendliness of wood as a fuel.

One of the disadvantages of wood burning boilers is the size of the flue needed to discharge the waste gases as well as the ventilation needed to the boiler compartment. A large storage area with sprinkler system may also be needed for the fuel. There has however been great advances made in the size and quality of the equipment suitable for church use and where a year ago, this type of installation would not have been feasible, I think today it is worthy of full investigation.

Bio diesel

Bio diesel is produced from a variety of organic material; usually vegetable oils, in the UK it is mainly oil seed rape. I must admit, I always wondered what they did with those large fields of golden yellow flowers that you see as you travel down the motorway.

It is carbon neutral as although carbon dioxide is released when it is burned as it is with any other fuel, this is offset by the amount of carbon absorbed while the plant was alive.

At the time of writing, I have to say that this is not produced commercially in very large quantities and as a result it is expensive in relation to other fuels. However the environmental friendliness is heavily debated. Some would argue that the CO_2 released during the production of the fertiliser that is placed on the fields and the transport associated with the production of the fuel is in excess of that saved.

There are also of course advantages to bio diesel:

- It has a higher flash point than fossil fuels.

- Unlike fossil fuels it is completely biodegradable and non-toxic.

- It is also relatively easy and cheap to install either a new boiler to burn it, or with only a little modification needed you can convert your existing oil-fired boiler.

Surprisingly Brazil is one of the leading countries in the production of bio fuel. It is generally derived from sugar cane, which is produced in large quantities and for which, there are few other uses these days.

I think that just about covers renewable energies in relation to your church. Of course there are other renewable energies, such as wave or tidal power and hydro-power, but these are not relevant to us at the moment. I would also imagine that you may be suffering from information over-load at the moment and are a little dazed by it all.

If after all avenues have been exhausted and you find that switching to renewable energy is not possible there is another alternative.

Currently 2% of the UK's energy is provided from renewable sources such as wind and solar power. The 6 main energy companies will allow you to pay extra for them to provide more energy from these renewable sources. You still get the same electricity as before but the company will put the extra money into procuring energy from renewable sources not coal or gas or nuclear.

8 Environmentally Friendly Shopping

When we go shopping, whether it is for ourselves or for the church, there are a number of measures that we can introduce to make shopping more environmentally friendly. I remember when I was first diagnosed as being diabetic how it changed my shopping experience. I took to reading every label on the supermarket shelf deciding if it was suitable before putting it in the basket.

The same happened when I became environmentally aware; a similar scenario began but I was looking for different attributes. I now check the provenance of a product - packaging, origin of produce, biodegradability and several other factors before I purchase.

There are a whole host of issues that need to be considered when buying any product. When talking about reducing the carbon footprint everyone thinks about saving energy around the home but the products that we buy and use every week contribute to that footprint by releasing carbon emissions during production and transport.

Biodegradable products:

Biodegradation is the process by which organic substances are broken down by the enzymes produced by living organisms. The term is often used in relation to ecology, waste management and environmental remediation (bioremediation). Organic material can be degraded aerobically, with oxygen, or anaerobically, without oxygen.

A term related to biodegradation is biomineralisation, in which organic matter is converted into minerals.

Biodegradable matter is generally organic material such as plant and animal matter and other substances originating from living organisms, or artificial materials that are similar enough to plant and animal matter to be put to use by microorganisms.

Engineered landfills are designed with liners to prevent toxic waste seeping into the surrounding soil and groundwater. Paper and other materials that normally degrade in a few years degrade more slowly over longer periods of time. In modern landfills biogas can be collected and used for power generation. Biogas contains methane which has approximately 21 times the global warming potential of carbon dioxide.

Plastics in particular can stay in the environment for hundreds of years before breaking down. Check the type of plastic in both the product and packaging. Sometimes the packaging will tell you that it is degradable but this is very different to biodegradable. Biodegradable means it may be broken down naturally by other living organisms. Waste that cannot be broken down by other living organisms may be called non-biodegradable. Degradable products are products that are capable of being broken down in stages usually only after the introduction of an external influence, such as a chemical.

Names to look out for are PSM or plastarch material or PLA polylactide as these truly are biodegradable and can be composted.

Now here are some startling facts - well they were startling to me, these are the times it takes for some common products to break down in the earth under normal conditions. The biodegradable times of common non- plastic items are as follows:

Banana skins	2 – 10 days
Cotton rags	1 – 5 months
Sugarcane Pulp Products	30 – 60 days
Paper	2 – 5 months
Rope	3 – 14 months
Orange Peel	6 months
Wool Socks	1 – 5 years
Leather Shoes	25 – 40 years
Tin Cans	50 - 100 years
Aluminium Cans	80 - 100 years

Here are biodegradable times for some plastic based materials:

Plastic bags	10 – 20 years
Tetrapacks – ie Milk cartons	5 years
Cigarette filters	1 – 12 years
Nylon fabric	30 – 40 years
Plastic six-pack holder rings	450 years
Disposable nappies/sanitary napkins	500 – 800 years
Plastic Bottles	non-biodegradeable
Styrofoam cup	non-biodegradeable

It is incredible but there are a shocking 46,000 pieces of plastic floating in every square mile of ocean killing 1 million sea birds, 100,000 sea mammals and countless fish each year. This has come from years of dumping waste products at sea.

In order to reduce this waste, before you purchase a product ask yourself if it can be recycled. Check the packaging to make sure it is made of recycled material and can be easily recycled at your local centre. All packaging should tell you if it can be recycled or if it is biodegradable and include safe disposal instructions for chemicals and toxic products.

You should ask yourself these questions:

- Is the product been from a sustainable source? Is a natural resource being used up to create this product or its packaging? If so do I really need it?

- Is it sourced ethically? Are any workers involved being treated well and getting a fair deal? Are any animals both wild and livestock being treated humanely.

- How far has the product travelled, what is the carbon footprint? It is usually better to buy locally produced products wherever possible they have travelled less and so have a lower carbon footprint.

A good idea is to spend a little time researching the policies of a few of the companies and products you buy regularly. See if regulators and environmental charities have anything to say about them. You can then make informed choices as to which products fit in with both your own beliefs and with that of the church.

Below are some common issues with products that are regularly bought by churches:

- Cleaning chemicals: Whether these are soaps, disinfectants or bleach they can all have a detrimental effect once released into the environment. There is a lot to be said for the more traditional methods of cleaning, lemon juice and bicarbonate of soda are always useful to have about. An environmentally friendly option for cleaning glass and silverware would be to use vinegar and crumpled-up newspaper.

- Banking and Insurance: What ethical policies do your bank and insurance company adopt, do they conflict with your own values as a Christian? Scrutinise these people closely, check whom they sponsor. Do the companies they sponsor have proper ethical values?

- What about church activities. After service do you serve tea and coffee? Is it fair trade produce? Is it served in traditional cups and saucers. Plastic cups and plates although easy to use have a detrimental effect on the environment. It is so easy to fall into the convenient throw away society that we have.

You need to also remember that cakes and biscuits along with many other common products contain palm oil. Palm oil comes from the islands of Indonesia where vast areas of rainforest are cut down to grow the palms each year, threatening the wildlife there, which includes a huge number of species including the Sumatran tiger (of which there are less than 400 left) and our close relative the orang-utan. The sad thing is that once the rainforest has gone it will never return; the soil of the palm fields is eroded until very little will grow there, not even palm oils hence the never ending expansion into the forest

If you do not already use Fair-trade products for after service refreshments you should make that change! You will know that the both the environment and the lives of subsistence farmers in developing countries will benefit.

Fair trade is an organized social movement and has a market-based approach to alleviating global poverty and promoting sustainability. The movement advocates the payment of a fair price as well as social and environmental standards in areas related to the production of a wide variety of goods. It focuses in particular on exports from the developing countries to developed countries, most notably handicrafts, coffee, cocoa, sugar, tea, bananas, honey, cotton, wine, fresh fruit and flowers.

Fair trade's strategic intent is to deliberately work with marginalized producers and workers in order to help them move from a position of vulnerability to security and economic self-sufficiency. It also aims at empowering them to become stakeholders in their own organizations and actively play a wider role in the global arena to achieve greater equity in international trade.

Fair trade proponents include a wide array of international religious, development aid, social and environmental organizations such as Oxfam, Amnesty International and Caritas International.

Like most developmental efforts, fair trade has proven itself controversial and has drawn criticism from both ends of the political spectrum. Some economists and conservative think tanks see fair trade as a type of subsidy. Segments of the left criticize fair trade for not adequately challenging the current trading system.

In 2007, Fair trade certified sales amounted to approximately €2.3 billion (US $3.62 billion) worldwide, a 47% year-to-year increase. While this represents less than one hundredth of a percentage point of world trade in physical merchandise, Fair trade products generally account for 0.5-5% of all sales in their product categories in Europe and North America. In May 2008, over 1.5 million disadvantaged producers worldwide were directly benefiting from fair trade while an additional 5 million benefited from fair trade funded infrastructure and community development projects.

Fair trade labeling (usually simply Fair trade) is a certification system designed to allow consumers to identify goods which meet agreed standards.

Overseen by a standard-setting body (FLO International) and a certification body (FLO-CERT), the system involves independent auditing of producers and traders to ensure the agreed standards are met.

For a product to carry either the International Fair trade Certification Mark or the Fair Trade Certified Mark, it must come from FLO-CERT inspected and certified producer organizations. The crops must be grown and harvested in accordance with the international Fair trade standards set by FLO International. The supply chain must also have been monitored by FLO-CERT, to ensure the integrity of labeled products.

Fair trade certification guarantees not only fair prices, but also the principles of ethical purchasing. These principles include adherence to ILO agreements such as those banning child and slave labour, guaranteeing a safe workplace and the right to unionise, adherence to the United Nations charter of human rights, a fair price that covers the cost of production and facilitates social developmentand protection and conservation of the environment. The Fair trade certification system also promotes long-term business relationships between buyers and sellers, crop pre-financing and greater transparency throughout the supply chain and more.

The International Fair trade Certification Mark was launched in 2002 by FLOand replaced twelve Marks used by various Fair trade labeling initiatives. The new Certification Mark is currently used worldwide (with the exception of Canada and the United States).

The best way to ensure you buy products, which are sourced sustainably, ethically and are environmentally friendly, is to ask questions and research the manufacturers and producers. See what they have to say and what others have to say about them. Only then can you make an informed choice. Too many people don't question where the products that fill our supermarket shelves come from and the church as a moral authority for the majority should lead the way.

9 Recycling

Perhaps a little belatedly we now seem to be taking the whole recycling scenario more seriously both in the home and commercially. So complicated is the disposal of rubbish at Dunphy Towers that Mrs Dunphy is the only person in the house qualified to sort the waste into the appropriate repository!

The council have issued us with the following receptacles:

- A brown wheelie bin for the garden waste.
- A bright green wheelie bin for plastics, bottles and cans.
- Large blue plastic bags for waste paper (and *not* sweet wrappers as I have been told) magazines and the like.
- A box for used batteries.
- A dark green wheelie bin for household rubbish that does not fall into any of the afore mentioned categories.

At the re-cycling centre at the local shopping precinct there are even more bins. One for shoes, one for clothing, glass can be separated into various colours, aluminium cans and paper.

Also at the local waste-management centre there are sections for more hazardous waste i.e. fridges, televisions, computer monitors, fluorescent tubes.

Our local optician collects spectacles to be sent to developing countries – having the gift of sight is more important to them than the latest fashion and even mobile phones can be recycled.

It seems that there is very little that cannot be used again or put to good use elsewhere instead of draining what resources we have left. As a society in general we are far too wasteful.

Recycling is one of the simplest ways to reduce your carbon footprint and help the environment; it takes far less energy to turn used aluminium cans into more aluminium cans than it does to create one from scratch, the same applies to paper and plastics. Less land has to be used for landfill, less plastics etc are released into the environment where they cause damage, particularly if non biodegradable.

I think that a church should not only recycle church waste, but also encourage the congregation to do the same. If the lack of understanding and the complexity of recycling are daunting, direct the congregation to the local council website which should detail exactly what and where materials can be recycled in the local area.

As I have just demonstrated with my own domestic situation, recycling can be heavily complicated, every council and borough has a different system and set of rules. Finding out where your local recycling centre is and what the rules are is not usually too difficult, however determining exactly what can and cannot be recycled can be a little more complicated with many types of packaging being made from a combination of materials not all of which can be recycled.

This is often cited as the major reason people choose not to recycle or not recycle more. As mentioned in the previous chapter this can be reduced and prevented by careful selection when buying products to ensure the packaging is kept to a minimum and made from materials that can be readily recycled. In the present climate of environment awareness many companies publish recycling information on their packaging, which is often ignored as few people know what the recycling symbols mean, as there are many different types. Some tell you simply that the packaging can be recycled, others that it has to be recycled in a certain way others tell you the packaging is made from a percentage of recycled material and it doesn't help that all these symbols look very similar.

The most common ones to look out for are listed below:

The tidy man symbol simply asks you to dispose of the packaging thoughtfully and not litter. This is probably the most common symbol found on packaging.

This symbol will be found on glass bottles etc and means please place in bottle bank. Glass comes in 3 colours clear, green and brown and many recycling centres usually have a bottle bank for each type.

This symbol is found mainly on drinks cans and other aluminium packaging and should be disposed of at an aluminium recycling point.

This symbol means the product is made from recyclable steel and so must be recycled separately from other metals such as aluminium. As a general rule food tins are steel and drinks cans are aluminium. A good way to test this if there is no symbol is to use a magnet; steel is magnetic whereas aluminium is not. Other types of metal container such as aerosols can be recycled but must be completely empty before hand. Metal film such as foil and sweet wrappers cannot be recycled.

The Mobius Loop is one of the most common symbols and simply means the packaging can be recycled. The Mobius Loop with a % inside indicates what percentage of the packaging is made from recycled materials. This is however voluntary and not all packaging containing recycled material has it.

The UK's symbol for recycling found on packaging and recycling points.

The green dot shows that a recovery fee has been paid for this packaging in some European countries.

The crossed out wheelie bin is usually found on electrical items and batteries and indicates these items need to be disposed of separately at your local household waste-recycling centre.

The following symbols indicate which type of plastic the packaging is made from and this determines if and how can be recycled or not.

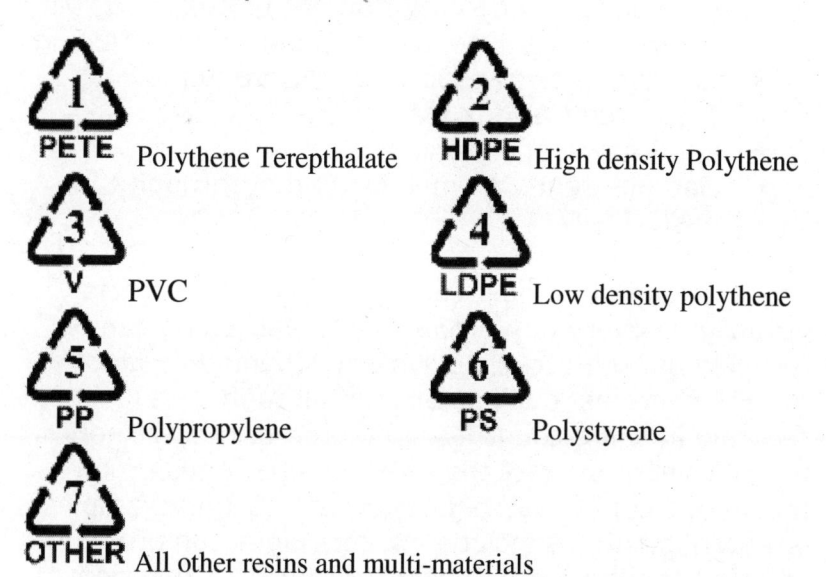

PETE Polythene Terepthalate

HDPE High density Polythene

V PVC

LDPE Low density polythene

PP Polypropylene

PS Polystyrene

OTHER All other resins and multi-materials

107

Plastic bags should be reused and once worn out recycled at the supermarket; most now have a specialised recycling point. The government has recently announced plans for supermarkets to charge for plastic bags so the best option will soon be not to use them at all but take bags with you to the supermarket instead of using theirs.

Paper in any form from cardboard to printer paper can be recycled at most centres, however it is beneficial to source paper as far as possible from sustainably managed forests and/or previously recycled paper to save what is left of the world's forests and woodlands.

Other ways to reduce paper waste:

- Set your printer to print on both sides
- Reuse old paper etc as scrap paper or packaging for storing or transporting delicate items.
- Try to reduce junk mail
- Read newspapers online
- Get bills sent via email instead of through the post.

These are just the most common recyclable objects virtually all every day products and packaging can be recycled but our recycling system is behind much of the EU where as much as 50% of all rubbish is recycled in some countries compared to the 17% of the UK. Yet it is a fact that 60% of what ends up on the landfill could have been recycled. Other examples of recyclable items include ink cartridges can often be recycled at the recycling point or refilled at your local computer store. Organic waste i.e. food and garden waste should be composted.

The whole purpose of recycling is so that items get reused in order to complete a cycle. One way to encourage recycling is to buy recycled products or products with packaging that is also made from recycled materials. Once you have finished with it recycle both the product and packaging and the cycle continues.

A good way for the church to encourage recycling is to lead by example and get the congregation involved in recycling church waste by showing them how easy it can be. Also as the complexity and misunderstanding can dissuade people from making the effort, help to make it easier by asking people to bring reusable or recyclable items to collections at church.

Collections of books, toys, clothes, DVD's etc can be given to local charity shops to be reused. Other collections can be for items to recycle such as old mobile phones and ink cartridges, which people may not necessarily think of recycling otherwise.

You can even recycle for charity, there are many websites offering this service. Send them your empty ink cartridge or mobile phone and they will then donate money to the charity of your choice.

Many different materials can be recycled but each type requires a different technique. The following gives a list of the most common recyclable products and how they can be best dealt with.

Concrete and Aggregates

Concrete aggregate collected from demolition sites is put through a crushing machine, often along with asphalt, bricks, dirt and rocks. Smaller pieces of concrete are used as gravel for new construction projects. Crushed, recycled concrete can also be used as the dry aggregate for brand new concrete if it is free of contaminants. This reduces the need for other rocks to be dug up, which in turn saves trees and habitats.

Batteries

Some batteries contain toxic heavy metals, making recycling or proper disposal a high priority. The large variation in size and type of batteries makes their recycling extremely difficult: they must first be sorted into similar kinds and each kind requires an individual recycling process. Additionally, older batteries contain mercury and cadmium, harmful materials which must be handled with care. Due to their potential environmental damage, proper disposal of used batteries is required by law in many areas. Unfortunately, this mandate has been difficult to enforce.

Lead-acid batteries, like those used in cars are relatively easy to recycle and many regions have legislation requiring vendors to accept used products. In the United States, the recycling rate is 90%, with new batteries containing up to 80% recycled material in the U.K. it is a little lower

Garden waste

Kitchen, garden and other green waste can be recycled into useful material by composting. This process allows natural aerobic bacteria to break down the waste into fertile topsoil. Much composting is done on a household scale, but municipal green-waste collection programs also exist. These programs can supplement their funding by selling the topsoil produced.

Computers and electrical

The direct disposal of electrical equipment — such as old computers and mobile phones — is banned in many areas due to the toxic contents of certain components. The recycling process works by mechanically separating the metals, plastics and circuit boards contained in the appliance. When this is done on a large scale at an electronic waste recycling plant, component recovery can be achieved in a cost-effective manner. Most local authorities have a dedicated area where these can be deposited

Steel

Iron and steel are the world's most recycled materials and are among the easiest materials to reprocess, as they can be separated magnetically from the waste stream. Recycling is via a steelworks: scrap is either re-melted in an Electric Arc Furnace (90-100% scrap), or used as part of the charge in a Basic Oxygen Furnace (around 25% scrap).

Any grade of steel can be recycled to top quality new metal, with no 'downgrading' from prime to lower quality materials as steel is recycled repeatedly.
42% of crude steel produced is recycled material. It is unlikely that you are likely to be involved in this in your everyday church life, but should you re making any changes to your building you may wish to ensure that your architect or builder deals with waste metals in the correct manner.

Aluminium

Aluminium is shredded and ground into small pieces or crushed into bales. These pieces or bales are melted in an aluminum smelter to produce molten aluminium. By this stage the recycled aluminium is indistinguishable from new aluminium and further processing is identical for both. This process does not produce any change in the metal, so aluminium can be recycled indefinitely.

Recycling aluminium saves 95% of the energy cost of processing new aluminium This is because the temperature necessary for melting recycled, nearly pure, aluminium is 600°C, while to extract mined aluminium from its ore requires 900°C. To reach this higher temperature, much more energy is needed, leading to the high environmental benefits of aluminium recycling.

Glass

Glass bottles and jars are gathered via curbside collection schemes and bottle banks, where the glass may be sorted into colour categories.

The collected glass is taken to a glass recycling plant where it is monitored for purity and contaminants are removed. The cullet is crushed and added to a raw material mix in a melting furnace. It is then mechanically blown or molded into new jars or bottles. Glass cullet is also used in the construction industry for aggregate and glassphalt. Glassphalt is a road-laying material which comprises around 30% recycled glass. Glass can be recycled indefinitely as its structure does not deteriorate when reprocessed.

Paper

Paper can be recycled by reducing it to pulp and combing it with pulp from newly harvested wood. As the recycling process causes the paper fibres to breakdown, each time paper is recycled its quality decreases. This means that either a higher percentage of new fibres must be added, or the paper down-cycled into lower quality products. Any writing or colouration of the paper must first be removed by de-inking, which also removes fillers, clays and fiber fragments.

Almost all paper can now be recycled, but some types are harder to recycle than others. Papers coated with plastic or aluminium foil and papers that are waxed, pasted, or gummed are usually not recycled because the process is too expensive. Gift wrap paper also cannot be recycled due to the fact that it is already low quality.

Sometimes recyclers ask for the removal of the glossy inserts from newspapers because they are a different type of paper.

Glossy inserts have a heavy clay coating that some paper mills cannot accept. Most of the clay is removed from the recycled pulp as sludge which must be disposed. If the coated paper is 20% by weight clay, then each ton of glossy paper produces more than 200kg of sludge and less than 800kg of fiber.

Plastics

Plastic recycling is the process of recovering scrap or waste plastics and reprocessing the material into useful products. Compared to glass or metallic materials, plastic poses unique challenges due to the massive number of types of plastic, they each carry a resin identification code and must be sorted before they can be recycled. This can be costly – while metals can be sorted using electromagnets, there is no such 'easy sorting' capability that exists for plastics. In addition to this, whilst labels do not need to be removed from bottles for recycling, lids are often made from a different kind of non-recyclable plastic.

Textiles

When considering textile recycling, one must understand what the material consists of. Most textiles are composites of cotton (biodegradable material) and synthetic plastics. Many international organisations collect used textiles from developed countries as a donation to those third world countries. This recycling practice is encouraged because it helps to reduce unwanted waste while providing clothing to the needy.

Damaged textiles are further sorted into grades to make industrial wiping cloths and for use in paper manufacture or material suitable for fibre reclamation and filling products.

Fibre reclamation mills sort textiles according to fibre type and colour. Colour sorting eliminates the need to re-dye the recycled textiles. The textiles are shredded into "shoddy" fibres and blended with other selected fibres, depending on the intended end use of the recycled yarn. The blended mixture is carded to clean and mix the fibres and spun ready for weaving or knitting. The fibres can also be compressed for mattress production. Textiles sent to the flocking industry are shredded to make filling material for car insulation, roofing felts, loudspeaker cones, panel linings and furniture padding.

Timber

Recycling timber has become popular due to its image as an environmentally friendly product, with consumers commonly believing that by purchasing recycled wood the demand for *green timber* will fall and ultimately benefit the environment. Greenpeace also view recycled timber as an environmentally friendly product, citing it as the most preferable timber source on their website. The arrival of recycled timber as a construction product has been important in both raising industry and consumer awareness towards deforestation and promoting timber mills to adopt more environmentally friendly practices

10 Greening up the Churchyard

Of the hundreds of churches I visit a year many have some outdoor space; whether it is a churchyard, graveyard or simply just a car park. Making use of this space for wildlife is another way that you can help the environment.

Graveyards in particular are known to be havens for wildlife as they often closely resemble natural meadows; with infrequently cut grass in which wild flowers and the occasional tree will grow, attracting insects, birds and small mammals; attracting wildlife has many benefits.

Planting outdoor areas with wild flowers will not only provide food for insects and thus the rest of the food chain but also provide fresh flowers for decoration inside throughout the year. Choose species carefully selecting native British species to ensure year round cover and aim to have at least once species flowering or providing food at any one time to ensure food throughout the year.

Putting up bird feeders and strategically placing bird, bat and insect boxes will encourage many species to feed, nest and hibernate. Bird and bat boxes come in a variety of shapes and sizes to suit the various sizes of different species. See which species your church already has in the vicinity before deciding which type of box to choose. Insect boxes come in two main types, the first is hibernation or over-wintering boxes, which consist of a variety of little nooks and cracks of various sizes that a whole variety of insects will crawl into and sleep through the lean cold months.

The second are bee boxes, which provide a home for a colony of bees.

Older church buildings in particular may be a haven for wildlife, providing nesting sites for birds and roosting places for bats living in the roof spaces. All species of bat in the UK are protected and so it is wise to get the advice of a local wildlife centre if you are planning on doing any work on or around roosts.

I can personally vouch for the importance of bat boxes because if they take a liking to the church fabric rather than a box, believe me it could cause all kinds of structural problems. I know a number of churches that have bat infestations and because they are a protected species they have their hands tied in solving the problem.

Using outdoor space doesn't have to be limited to wildlife; consider having outdoor services, prayer and church walks allow the congregation to be surrounded by the beauty of nature as well as being great social events.

Other outdoor events can include picnics or barbecues, church sales; car boot sales are great way of recycling those unwanted items and again raise funds for the church.

Such events can have these main aims:

- Worship and give praise for God's creation.
- Raise awareness and spread the word about of environmental issues.
- Real action to accomplish a goal by reducing carbon emissions or carbon footprint
- Raising money for an environmental charity or helping local wildlife.

Events and activities that get the entire congregation and the wider community involved in environmental issues are often great social events and also help to spread awareness. Acting as an example is one of the best way to encourage others to follow and spread the message.

Some have accused the church and world religions in general of being silent on environmental issues; this certainly is not the case as the environmental policies of a wide range of religious groups and projects such as Operation Noah show. This is unfortunately the impression a large majority of the population gets and needs to change.

Reducing the church carbon footprint should not be limited to simply the building; but to the homes and businesses of the entire congregation not simply to prevent global warming but as an example to others.

11 The Parish and the Community

A church plays a very big part of any community, be it a small country church in a rural location, or an inner city church at the hub of a conurbation. It is the focal point for many people and like it or not, are seen to be examples of what in some cases is a persons only contact with Christianity. We must therefore set a good example particularly in all things green. We should endeavour to communicate our message in the hope that other will follow.

If you have extensive church grounds with maybe a large car park, then why not have recycling bins sited there. It will encourage both church members to participate in recycling and will also attract non-church members of the community to visit your premises. This may also open up the opportunity to operate a joint venture with your local authority to encourage and promote other environmental issues.

Why not invite schools, youth groups, other organisations and community groups into discussions with you on environmental issues? Try to promote projects and initiatives that help the community to become more aware of environmental issues. To help achieve this you could publicise conservation events in your parish magazine and in church notices so that you can take your message to a wider audience.

Other areas that are important are transport issues. Everybody should think carefully about how they travel, taking into account the environmental impact of the different means of transport. as well as the consideration of cost, convenience and reliability.

The cheapest and healthiest method of transport has to be walking, however it is not always possible to walk everywhere so other methods have to be looked at.

Cycling is probably the next best option but as with walking this is not always possible, not everyone is fit and healthy enough to cope with physically demanding transport. Does your church provide a cycle rack for use of its parishioners?

Public transport is of course preferable to using a car but some areas have little or no public transport system, particularly in rural areas.

In some cases there is no option but to use the car but you can make changes, try and plan routes so that they are as short as possible, car share as much as possible, this not only cuts down on the environmental impact but on the financial side of motoring too.

- Does your church observe car free Sundays and Green Transport Weeks?
- Do your own parishioners car share wherever possible?

- If you have house groups do you give consideration to the accessibility of the location? I.e. for those who could walk, cycle, or use public transport.

All food for thought I am sure you will agree. Even the smallest of changes can and will have an impact.

A large active church has many committees and action groups, covering all of the fabric and spiritual matters within the parish, but do you have anyone in the church that can apply political pressure when required?

As well as taking action ourselves, we need to make sure that those who can shape the major political decisions know of our concerns

Our concerns regarding exhaust emissions, road building and the protection of the ozone layer are all important. It is always useful to be on friendly terms with your local councillor and MP, governments are sensitive to the concerns of voters and need their support to press for measures to be taken by the international community.

If you let them know that you are there either as a friend or a nuisance you can be assured they will listen to you. Say a prayer for them; they have a hard job too!

12 The Wider Community

It is commendable that we try and do all we can to save the environment but we must not forget those who share the planet with us. Our own demands for the cheapest clothing and variety of choice of food mean that we have an impact on the lives of other nations, even if they live thousands of miles away. We have a responsibility to those in the developing world to give them a fair chance.

How would you answer these questions?

- Does your church actively support campaigns about world poverty, living conditions, environmental issues and human rights?

- Does your church sell Fair trade (Tradecraft) products? I know several churches that do this on a monthly basis after their main service; this makes a little income for the church but also promotes Fair trade products to a larger audience.

- Do you support the work of aid groups and justice development agencies, such as Tear Fund, Christian Aid and CAFOD etc?

- Do you support those charities closer to home dealing with the homeless i.e. Shelter or Crisis.

Forgive me if I am pushing against an open door, but I feel it is important to mention all these issues. Some churches are excellent in all these areas, but others may be unaware of just exactly where they can make a telling contribution. This is just to bring to the fore just some of the areas in which we can all make a difference by making small changes to our daily lives.

Conclusions

God has given us a responsibility to look after the planet, so we must try to reduce the impact that we are having on the environment. There are many ways to reduce the Carbon footprint of your church. The first step is to carry out an audit to see how green your church actually is.

Making your energy supply more efficient, hopefully from a renewable source is a huge step towards reducing you carbon footprint but any major work needs to be considered carefully especially if dealing with an older church building.

Energy efficient appliances should be fitted wherever possible to reduce the amount of energy burned.

Shop wisely most people already use some fair trade products but finding products that are not harmful to the environment is difficult. Palm oil is an ingredient in many mass-produced bakery products but huge areas of rainforest in Indonesia have been destroyed in order to grow the palms.

Cleaning chemicals are a difficult issue. Choose environmentally friendly products where possible or try using older traditional methods such as we have mentioned earlier in the book.

Buy products with as little packaging as possible and ensure what packaging there is can be recycled.

Re-use and recycle, encourage the congregation to recycle waste, rather than rely on the rubbish collection. Arrange to have a recycling station on the church grounds. This could be anything from just a few large boxes labelled plastics, aluminium, paper, etc to a bottle bank if you have adequate space. Your local authority may be willing to get involved in this further underlining your responsibility and leadership in the community. Have car boot sales; your unwanted item may just be the thing that someone else needs.

Make use of outdoor areas, graveyards are well known to be wildlife havens. Growing flowers will help wildlife by attracting insects and insect eaters and so establishing a flourishing ecosystem This need not be expensive and often keen gardeners within the congregation will be only too happy to help.

Put up bird, bat and insect boxes you will provide homes and winter hibernation places for a variety of wildlife.

Raise environmental issues during sermons; make the congregation aware of what the church is doing to help the environment and how they can get involved. Get out into the local community and let them know what you are doing to help the environment

The United Reformed Church Resolution 19

The Environment

The United Reformed Church has kindly given us permission to reproduce their Resolution 19 on the environment. I would like to acknowledge and thank them for their agreement.

General Assembly

a) Affirms its commitment to the Five Marks of Mission with their call to the people of God to be faithful stewards of God's creation and to seek to sustain and renew the life of the earth

b) Welcomes and endorses 'An environmental policy for the United Reformed Church'

c) Commends churches that have engaged with the United Reformed Church 'Roots and Branches' pack and the subsequent ecumenical 'Eco-Congregation' project; congratulates Zion United Reformed Church Northallerton and Christ Church URC/Methodist Church Ross-on-Wye on gaining the Eco-Congregation Award; and encourages other churches to follow their lead

d) Pledges its support for Operation Noah, an initiative of the Christian Ecology Link seeking to raise awareness of and promote action around, the issue of climate change.

An Environmental Policy for the United Reformed Church

1 Introduction

1.1 For the past five or more years the United Reformed Church has been engaged in a thorough examination of its ideas of mission and the degree to which ideas are turned into reality in the life of the Church. One of the tools used has been The Five Marks of Mission, first formulated by the Lambeth Conference of 1988 and then endorsed in their present form in 1997 by the Forum of Churches Together in England:

To proclaim the good news of the Kingdom

To teach, baptise and nurture new believers

To respond to human need by loving service

To seek to transform unjust structures of society

To strive to safeguard the integrity of creation; and to sustain and renew the life of the earth

1.2 General Assembly adopted the Five Marks in 1999. These principles need to be translated into policy and an agenda for the church. Church and Society has prepared the following environmental policy in response to the fifth 'mark', 'to strive to safeguard the integrity of creation; to sustain and renew the life of the earth'. It is offered to Assembly for discussion and (hopefully) adoption.

1.3 It is clear from all that we affirm that care for creation, a just sharing of the world's resources and a concern for the environment are fundamental gospel commitments. We acknowledge the work and effort already undertaken by some of our local churches on environmental/creation care issues and noting the significant impact that this has had on their mission, believe that a far greater number should be encouraged to give expression to their Christian faith in this way. Assembly is therefore invited to reflect upon and to affirm the following policy statement in order that it may guide thinking and practice within our local churches, districts, synods, colleges and national church life and practice.

2 Our Stewardship of Creation

2.1 The Basis of Union, paragraph 17, affirms that the United Reformed Church believes '....in the one living and true God, creator, preserver and ruler of all things in heaven and earth, Father, Son and Holy Spirit....' God entrusts creation to our stewardship (Genesis 1-2) and in Christ wills to reclaim it from its bondage to decay (Romans 8:19-25). Discipleship involves caring for creation so that future generations (whom God also loves) can enjoy it and benefit from it.

2.2 We affirm that Christian mission includes caring for God's earth and of all creation. It includes sharing in putting right the relationships within God's creation that have gone wrong and working within the church and with partners outside the church to grow towards justice and good stewardship as envisaged in the Biblical vision of the world as it is meant to be.

2.3 We know that human activity has contributed to the degradation of the earth in its land seas and atmosphere and that this is not the will of God. We believe that this degradation limits the attainment of the fullness of life that God wills for all creation and is a sin for which we should seek forgiveness. It also imposes most heavily upon the peoples of the developing countries of the world and is part of the intrinsic injustice to which we bear witness.

2.4 In fulfilling our commitment to our calling we challenge and encourage our churches and members to care for the earth by following sustainable practice and by taking into account global and local environmental considerations for present and future generations

In the conservation and use of resources in church life and at home

In following a more sustainable lifestyle

In active involvement in community initiatives aimed at sustaining and renewing the environment

In concerns for action on global environmental issues

2.5 To this end we should have regard to

The challenge of meeting the needs of the present without compromising the ability of future generations to meet their needs

The potential for harnessing the skills, expertise and enthusiasm of the members of our congregations

The opportunities for co-operation in joint initiatives with other congregations, including ecumenical joint action, schools and secular organisations

The actions in one place that may have an effect in other places

The valuable contribution of small steps by individuals as well as major initiatives.

3 Our Environmental Objectives

3.1 In order to work out our faith and fulfil our responsibility for the stewardship of God's creation, we commit ourselves to the following actions:

3.2 Awareness and Commitment

Promoting awareness among our congregations of these principles and objectives and of the values underpinning them

Ensuring that all staff members of the United Reformed Church, its synods and colleges are familiar with this environmental commitment and its objectives and encouraging them to work towards its implementation

Encouraging United Reformed Churches in their activities to comply with all relevant environmental recommendations for good practice

3.3 Energy and Water

Ensuring energy is used efficiently and whenever possible conserving and reducing its use

Encouraging the increased use of renewable energy, especially green electricity using water efficiently and with care

Preventing pollutants from entering the drainage system.

3.4 Waste

Reducing the production of material waste including unnecessary packaging

Encouraging the re-use, repair and re-cycling of materials including organic waste

Disposing of waste in a safe and responsible way

Adopting environmentally sensitive purchasing policies, for example recycled paper.

3.5 Materials and Resources

Buying products which are made in accordance with the principle of using material in a sustainable way and using locally-made or produced goods and food as far as this is possible and practicable

Buying products from sources that adhere to principles of fair trade, especially mindful of those within poorer countries

Taking into account the lifetime costs and embodied energy of materials when repairing, altering or rebuilding premises

Offering electronic communication as an alternative to paper for those who are suitably equipped

3.6 Natural and Built Environment

Taking appropriate opportunities to conserve and enhance the natural and built environment

Engaging with local planning developments where these affect the environment

Encouraging the renewal and enhancement of the urban environment

Being sensitive to the impact of church activities on the local environment

Ensuring church-owned land is used in ways that will protect the environment

3.7 Travel

Making every effort to reduce air pollution and energy consumption resulting from the use of cars and planes by avoidance of unnecessary travel and the use of energy-efficient vehicles

Exploring undertaking the work of the denomination and local church in ways which reduce the need for travel, particularly by car and plane and encouraging the use of public transport and sharing car transport whenever possible.

3.8 We affirm that the earth belongs to God and hold to a vision of a world that reflects the glory of God. So together we will celebrate all that is done and achieved in fulfilling our human responsibility for the care and stewardship of creation.

3.9 We recognise and commend

Eco-Congregation, an environmental toolkit for local churches which was established by the partnership of the Environmental Issues Network of Churches Together in Britain and Ireland and ENCAMS. Eco-Congregation now operates in England and Wales from the Arthur Rank Centre and in Scotland from a partnership between the Church of Scotland's Society, Religion and Technology Project and Keep Scotland Beautiful. (www.ecocongregation.org)

Operation Noah, an initiative of the Christian Ecology Link seeking to raise awareness of and promote action around, the issue of Climate Change. (www.christian-ecology.org.uk/noah)

3.10 These projects supply materials and assistance in raising the awareness of congregations to our stewardship of creation, for enhancing worship and Bible study, for working with children, young people and adults and for taking action of a practical nature in our church life and within our communities. We encourage their use amongst our churches as a way of living out our environmental policy.

We also commend the Roots and Branches pack produced by the Church and Society Committee of the United Reformed Church in 1999.

We thank the Baptist Union for permission to model the above Environmental Policy on theirs.

Further Sources of Information

Contacts:

Action for a Global Climate Community: a non-profit organisation based in London
Details: www.climatecommunity.org

Alliance of Religions and Conservation: a secular body that helps major religions of the world to develop their own environmental programmes founded in 1995 by HRH Prince Philip.
Details: www.arcworld.org/

A Rocha: International Christian nature conservation organisation.
Details: www.arocha.org

BBC Green Room: Articles from the BBC about the environment
Details: news.bbc.co.uk/1/hi/in_depth/sci_tech/green_room/default.stm

Campaign against Climate Change:
http://www.campaigncc.org

Christian Aid: Christian organisation dedicated to fighting poverty and injustice and the effects of climate change in the third world.
Details: www.christian-aid.org.uk

Christian Ecology Link: Christian environmental organisation based in the UK
Details: www.christian-ecology.org.uk.

Churches Together in Britain and Ireland: Churches working together to co-ordinate the work they do.
Details: www.ctbi.org.uk/

Church of England: 'Reducing the Carbon Footprint'
Details: www.shrinkingthefootprint.cofe.anglican.org
Email: shrinkingthefootprint@c-of-e.org.uk
Address: Shrinking the Footprint
         MPA Division
         Archbishops' Council
         Church House
         Great Smith Street
         London, SW1P 3NZ

Creation Challenge: Collaboration between many different Christian organisations mainly the Methodist and United reformed Churches
Details: www.creationchallenge.org.uk

Eco-congregation: an ecumenical programme helping churches make the link between environmental issues and Christian faith
Details: dependant on location:

For England and Wales

Jo Rathbone
Eco-congregation (England and Wales)
The Arthur Rank Centre
Stoneleigh Park
Warwickshire
CV8 2LZ
Tel: 024 0779 2491
Email: ecocongregation@arocha.org

Scotland

Margaret Warnock
Eco-Congregation Scotland
Keep Scotland Beautiful Project
Islay House
Livilands Lane
Stirling FK8 2BG
Tel: 01786 471333
Email: margaret.warnock@ksbscotland.org.uk

Or

Eleanor Todd
Eco-congregation Scotland
Society, Religion and Technology
121 George Street
Edinburgh EH2 4YN
Tel: 0131 240 2250

Ireland

The Presbyterian Representative

Mr Joe Furphy
Tel: +44 (0)28 9061 2311
Email: joe.fury@ecocongregationireland.org

The Roman Catholic Representative

Catherine Brennan SSL
Tel: +353 (0)87 259 9071
Fax: +353 (0)1 492 8240
Email: catherinebrennan@ecocongregationireland.org

The Church of Ireland Representative

Revd David Humphries
Tel: +44 (0)28 9048 2292[H]
Tel: +44 (0)28 9041 9171[O]
Email: david.Humphries@ecocongregationireland.org

The Methodist Representative

Mrs Helen Shiel
Tel: +353 (0)1 295 5032
Email: Helen.shiel@ecocongregationireland.org

Religious Society of Friends in Ireland (Quakers) Representative

Ms Natasha Harty
Tel: +353 (0)21 4652 429
Email: natasha.harty@ecocongregationireland.org

Environmental Policy of the Baptist Church
Details: www.baptist.org.uk/Resources/resource_downloads/312.PDF

Environmental policy of the Church of England
Details: www.shrinkingthefootprint.cofe.anglican.org/

Environmental policy of the Methodist Church
Details: www.creationchallenge.org.uk/enmcpolicy.htm/enmcpolicy.htm

Environmental policy of the Roman Catholic Church
Details: ww.life4seekers.co.uk/lifestylevalues/ecocatholic.html

Or

Catholic Enquiry Office (CEO)
114 West Heath Road
London, NW3 7TX
Tel: 0208 458 3316   Fax: 0208 905 5780
Email: enquiries@life4seekers.co.uk

The Environmental policy of the United Reformed Church   Details:
www.creationchallenge.org.uk/enurcpolicy.htm

Gaia Communications ARK Tariff: Gaia Communications together with Christian Aid have developed the Additional Renewable Kilowatt tariff. Offering environmental benefit to churches where green energies are in extremely short supply.
Details: www.gaia-energy.co.uk/ark.html

Intergovernmental Panel on Climate Change (IPCC): Provides regular analysis of the current state of scientific knowledge on climate change. Details: http://www.ipcc.ch/

International Institute for Environment and Development (IEED):
International policy research institute and non governmental body working for more sustainable and equitable global development.
Details: www.iied.org

Internuncio: an online resource with the objective of increasing understanding of the social implications of climate change to communities across the globe.
Details: http://www.internuncio.org

The John Ray Initiative - an educational charity bringing together scientific and Christian understandings of the environment.
Details: www.jri.org.uk

Live Simply: a project based on the idea that God calls us to live simply.
Details: www.livesimply.org.uk/

Lottery Fund

For information on (and how to apply for) big lottery fund breathing spaces grants.
Details: www.bbc.co.uk/breathingplaces

New Economics Foundation: aims to present economic analysis with people and the planet as the main considerations.
Details: www.neweconomics.org/gen/

The Noah Project: The only Jewish ecological group in Britain. It has support from all five major denominations and from secular Jews. Details: www.biggreenjewish.org/

The Omega Climate Change Course: A group from St Mark's Church, Broomhill and St Mary's, Bramall Lane, Sheffield, who encourage people to respond to the challenge of climate change. They have close links with various offices especially the Sheffield Campaign against Climate Change.
Details: www.omegaclimate.org.uk

Operation Noah: Christian charity raising awareness and lobbying government over environmental issues.
Details: www.operationnoah.org.

Also

Ark-in-a-Box: A resource pack for churches.
Details: www.christian-ecology.org.uk/noah/ark-in-a-box.htm

Revolutionary Cycling Cinema: A cinema powered by bicycle power. Demonstrating how to generate power locally and independently of fossil fuels
Details: cyclecinema.wordpress.com/

Stop Climate Chaos: a coalition of environmental and development NGOs.
Details: www.stopclimatechaos.org/default.asp

Tearfund: Christian charity aimed at relieving poverty and the effects of climate change in the third world can be found at   Details: www.tearfund.org

Transition towns:
Details: transitiontowns.org/

Further Reading

With regard to the subject of money and funding, which is usually in short supply in churches 'The Layman's Guide to Church Funding and Resources' is available through the same publishers direct via mail order.

Stop Climate Chaos: a coalition of environmental and development NGOs.
Details: www.stopclimatechaos.org/default.asp

Tearfund: Christian charity aimed at relieving poverty and the effects of climate change in the third world can be found at   Details: www.tearfund.org

Transition towns:
Details: transitiontowns.org/

Further Reading

With regard to the subject of money and funding, which is usually in short supply in churches 'The Layman's Guide to Church Funding and Resources' is available through the same publishers direct via mail order.

New Economics Foundation: aims to present economic analysis with people and the planet as the main considerations.
Details: www.neweconomics.org/gen/

The Noah Project: The only Jewish ecological group in Britain. It has support from all five major denominations and from secular Jews. Details: www.biggreenjewish.org/

The Omega Climate Change Course: A group from St Mark's Church, Broomhill and St Mary's, Bramall Lane, Sheffield, who encourage people to respond to the challenge of climate change. They have close links with various offices especially the Sheffield Campaign against Climate Change.
Details: www.omegaclimate.org.uk

Operation Noah: Christian charity raising awareness and lobbying government over environmental issues.
Details: www.operationnoah.org.

Also

Ark-in-a-Box: A resource pack for churches.
Details: www.christian-ecology.org.uk/noah/ark-in-a-box.htm

Revolutionary Cycling Cinema: A cinema powered by bicycle power. Demonstrating how to generate power locally and independently of fossil fuels
Details: cyclecinema.wordpress.com/